**E**NVIRONMENT &
**P**EOPLE
**I**NTEGRATED
**C**OURSE
**S**UPPLEMENTS

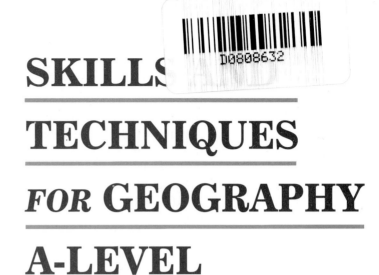

# SKILLS
# TECHNIQUES
## *FOR* GEOGRAPHY
## A-LEVEL

## Garrett Nagle
### With Michael Witherick

*Series Editor:*
Michael Witherick

STANLEY
THORNES

Stanley Thornes (Publishers) Ltd

First published in 1998 by:
Stanley Thornes (Publishers) Ltd
Ellenborough House
Wellington Street
CHELTENHAM GL50 1YW
England

00 01 02 / 10 9 8 7 6 5 4 3 2

A catalogue record for this book is available from the British Library.

ISBN 0-7487-3188-1

Designed by Giles Davies
Page layout and illustration by Hardlines, Charlbury, Oxford
Cover design by Sterling Associates
Cover photograph: Julian Cremona, Dale Fort Field Centre
Printed and bound in Great Britain by Martins The Printers Ltd,
Berwick upon Tweed

**Acknowledgements**

With thanks to the following for permission to reproduce copyright material in this book:

Associated Examinations Board, Figs 7.1, 7.3, 7.5, 7.6, 7.8; British Geological Survey, Fig. 4.4 (© NERC. All rights reserved.); London Examinations, a division of Edexcel Foundation, Figs 7.2, 7.4, 7.7, 7.9; *The Guardian*/James Meikle, Fig. 6.10; HMSO, © Crown copyright reproduced with permission of the Controller of Her Majesty's Stationary Office, Fig. 4.7; Oxford and County Newspapers, Fig. 6.9; Oxford University Press, Fig. 5.8.

The photographs in Figs. 4.14 (a), 6.3 and 6.5 were supplied by the author.

Every effort has been made to contact copyright holders. The publishers apologise to anyone whose rights have been inadvertently overlooked, and will be happy to rectify any errors or omissions.

# Contents

# Introduction

## The scope of modern Geography

Skills and techniques have always been an integral part of Geography. The current A-level and AS Geography syllabuses show that they are as much to the forefront of modern Geography as they have ever been. In order to put skills and techniques into some sort of perspective, it is worth asking (and answering) two important questions:

- What is Geography?
- What skills and techniques does studying the subject require?

Perhaps one of the best ways of defining Geography is to identify its major fields of study. These include:

- the physical characteristics of the environment (relief, climate, soils, etc.) and the processes that produce them;
- the human characteristics of the environment and the economic, social and political processes that produce them;
- the interaction of people and the environment – the impact of the physical environment on people, and the impact of people on the physical environment;
- spatial variations in the environment – differences from place to place;
- environmental changes over time.

There can be no questioning Geography's tremendous potential to be an exciting, topical and challenging subject. What other subject includes such a variety of topics – from environmental hazards to crime, from global warming to ghettos, from plate tectonics to inner-city decline? Geography really is a subject with a difference, for the following reasons:

- it crosses the divide between the arts, sciences and social sciences;
- it looks at relationships between people and the environment;
- it is concerned with all those contemporary issues and problems that lie rooted in the environment;
- it investigates differences in two different dimensions – changes in space (from place to place) and change over time;
- it investigates at a range of scales – spatially, from global to local, and temporally, from short-term to long-term;
- it involves analysing and summarising complex material drawn from a variety of sources;
- it makes full use of cartographic, statistical and visual techniques to support and illustrate its investigations.

# Skills

From the foregoing, we perhaps begin to see that the skills of the geographer will include the following:

- oral or verbal skills – discussing, explaining, arguing, etc.;
- judgmental skills – being able to evaluate conflicting views or evidence;
- written skills – producing essays, reports, etc.;
- fieldwork skills – collecting raw data, 'reading' the environment;
- statistical skills – processing, analysing and interpreting data in numerical form;
- cartographic and graphic skills – representing information and findings in the form of maps, graphs and other diagrams.

# Techniques

If the above are the skills of modern Geography, then what are its techniques? Techniques may be defined as the methods employed in the application or use of particular skills – they are the tools of skills.

It is in the last three skills areas noted above that techniques are particularly crucial. For example, the statistical skills of a geographer require knowledge of, and the ability to use properly, a whole range of techniques, such as chi-squared, nearest-neighbour analysis and significance tests. Choropleths, compound graphs and dispersion diagrams are some of the techniques utilised by the cartographic and graphic skills, whilst the fieldwork skills involve command of such diverse techniques as sampling, questionnaire design and slope measurement.

But perhaps the greatest skill of all in the present context is really knowing what techniques are available, how to use them and when to use them.

# The assessment of skills and techniques

In your forthcoming examinations you will be expected to show a command of most if not all of the skills and techniques outlined in **sections B** and **C** above. Of key importance is knowing what each technique can and cannot do, and when it is most appropriate to use it. Your understanding of all this and your skills proficiency will be tested in a number of different ways in the examination:

- in structured questions (for example, interpreting choropleth maps and triangular graphs);
- in data response questions (for example, reading map extracts and analysing photographs);
- in essay questions (for example, weighing up evidence and presenting reasoned arguments);
- in the personal investigation or project.

The last of these is by far the most important – most of the skills listed in **section B** will be put to use and assessed in the personal investigative study or project (sometimes also referred to as the individual or personal enquiry) that is now required by all A-level and most AS Geography syllabuses (see **Chapter 7**). Hopefully, what follows will help you to become more skilled, as well as more knowledgeable about and proficient in the use of selected geographical techniques.

# The scope of this book

This book concentrates on statistical, cartographic, graphical, and investigative techniques. Help with improving your learning and examination skills is available in another volume in the EPICS series – *Study Advice for Geography A-level*. Statistical techniques include **descriptive statistics**, such as mean, mode, median and standard deviation. More detailed **inferential statistics**, which draw conclusions or inferences about data, include Spearman's rank correlation coefficient, chi-squared and nearest-neighbour analysis. The cartographic methods covered by the book include choropleths, flow lines, isolines and sketch maps. The use of Ordnance Survey maps, satellite images, topological and mental maps lies outside the scope of this book, but may be found in a companion book entitled *Geographical Enquiries*. Graphical methods dealt with here are the widely used (and abused) techniques like bar and pie charts, dispersion diagrams and histograms, as well as a range of graphs – line, semi-log, polar, etc. Finally, this book focuses on the investigative skills needed in producing the personal investigation or individual project, namely the techniques of data collection (especially sampling and the use of questionnaires) and data analysis (such as hypothesis-testing and assessing significance).

This is not the sort of book to be read from cover to cover in strict sequence. Rather, it is more of a reference book to be consulted as and when you need to find out about specific skills and techniques. Hopefully you will find it a useful companion to the Geography core textbook *Environment and People*.

Much of the illustrative material in this book is based on student survey work undertaken in and around Oxford. It is hoped that this will demonstrate the variety of project work that is possible within a British town or city and its fringing countryside.

Finally, it needs to be stressed that what this book is about does not end when you have completed your examinations. Hopefully, you will find commanding these skills and techniques continues to be useful. Being able to:

- collect information
- assess the significance and reliability of information
- analyse and interpret information
- communicate effectively, visually as well as in the written and spoken word

are all skills that will serve you well in today's (and tomorrow's) workplace, where being able to gather, interpret, convey and make use of information are such important skills – truly life skills.

# Descriptive statistics

## Types of statistics

The word 'statistics' has two meanings. First, it refers to facts that are expressed in the form of numbers – collections of numerical information. The second meaning of the term is the science of drawing conclusions from numerical information – the collection, processing and interpretation of quantitative data.

There are innumerable types of statistics in the first sense. Almost every aspect of the natural world and human activity is now subjected to measurement in numerical terms. When it comes to the investigation of those measurements, there are two approaches: **descriptive statistics** and **inferential statistics**. Descriptive statistics seek to summarise data, whilst inferential statistics seek to identify relationships between sets of observations or measurements. Within both these branches, some statistical methods are easy to grasp and use, whilst others can be very complex.

**Descriptive statistics** include the **mean** or average of a data set, its **maximum** (highest value), **minimum** (lowest value), **range** (maximum to minimum), **mode** (the most frequently occurring number, group or class) and the **median** (the middle value when all the numbers are placed in ascending or descending rank order). In any project or enquiry, it is important to use these statistics, as they provide invaluable summaries of data, and are often the only statistics that are appropriate.

There are also four different types of **data**. (Please note immediately that data are plural; **datum** is singular.) **Nominal data** are objects which have names, for instance rock types, land uses or social groups. They would also include the dates of floods and famines, or the number of times particular events have occurred. These are the most basic type of data. In a personal investigative study we might categorise settlements as being hamlets, villages or towns, and then count the numbers of each to reveal a **hierarchy**. Alternatively, when studying urban functions, we may classify areas as industrial, commercial, residential, recreational, and so on. These may later be expressed as percentages of total land use.

Next come **ordinal** or **ranked data**. For example, the ranking of objects in ascending or descending order yields ordinal data. We might rank London, Birmingham and Manchester 1, 2 and 3 respectively in terms of the size of their populations, but having done so we need not know their exact sizes. Settlement hierarchies are often expressed in terms of ranks. One of the most commonly used statistics in Geography is Spearman's rank correlation coefficient, which compares two sets of ranked data. For example, we might be keen to investigate whether there is a relationship between a city's population size and the number of services it provides, or between pebble size in a stream bed and distance from the stream source.

**Interval** and **ratio data** both refer to real numbers. The difference between them, though, is important: with interval data there is no true zero. For example, if Oxford has a mean temperature of 13°C and Miami 26°C, it is not possible to state that Miami is twice as warm as Oxford, for if we had measured the temperatures in degrees Fahrenheit, the figures would have been 59°F and 79°F respectively. Ratio data, on the other hand, do possess a true zero. In these circumstances, it is possible to have 0mm rainfall, or a crop yield of 0kg. Thus it is possible to say that Miami, with 2 000mm of annual rainfall, is about three times as wet as Oxford, which has an annual rainfall of 670mm.

It is important to remember the general rule that nominal data (the simplest) can only yield quite simple, albeit important information, whereas more complicated data can be tested with more complex statistics.

## Review

1 What types of data are the following?
   a 16°C, 18°C, 30°C, –2°C.
   b 250mm, 4mm, 16mm, 0mm.
   c Drought, flood, famine, earthquake.
   d 1st, 2nd, =3rd, =3rd, 5th, 6th.
   e 1936, 1941, 1966, 1967, 1998.

---

# Summarising data

## Simple data

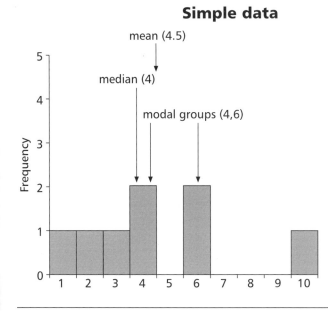

One of the most commonly used statistics is the **mean** or **average** (**Figure 2.1**). This is found by totalling the values for all observations ($\Sigma x$) and then dividing by the total number of observations ($n$): $\Sigma x/n$. For example, the number of services in eight villages was found to be 3, 10, 4, 6, 1, 4, 2, 6. The average is:

$$\frac{3 + 10 + 4 + 6 + 1 + 4 + 2 + 6}{8} = \frac{36}{8} = 4.5.$$

**Figure 2.1** Graph showing mean, median and modal groups

## Review

**2** The following rainfall measurements (in mm) were recorded over a one-week period:
4, 2, 1, 7, 5, 0, 2.

 **a** Plot the data on a graph similar to Figure 2.1.

 **b** Which of these statistics best summarises the data for these figures?

 **c** Which method is least satisfactory? Justify your choice.

Obviously, there cannot be half a service – or can there? Think, for example, of mobile shops, or post offices that only open for limited periods of time. So the mean is not always the best statistic to use.

The mode refers to the group or class which occurs most often (**Figure 2.1**). In this case both 4 and 6 occur twice – these are the modal groups. A pattern which has two peaks, as in this case, is called bimodal. Where there is one clear peak the distribution is known as unimodal.

Another method is to use the **median** (**Figure 2.1**). This is the middle value when all the data are placed in ascending or descending order, for instance 10, 6, 6, 4, 4, 3, 2, 1. In this case, because there are two middle values, we take the average of these two. They are both 4, hence the median is 4.

## Groups of data

Sometimes the data we collect are in group form. For example, we may have measured slope angles, or the ages of people, and slotted each value into one of the groups: 0–4, 5–9, 10–14, 15–19, etc. Finding an average is slightly more difficult. We use the midpoint of the group and multiply this by the frequency (**Figure 2.2**)

| Slope angle (°) | Midpoint ($x$) | Frequency ($f$) | Midpoint × frequency ($fx$) |
|---|---|---|---|
| 0 – 4 | 2 | 6 | 12 |
| 5 – 9 | 7 | 12 | 84 |
| 10 – 14 | 12 | 7 | 84 |
| 15 – 19 | 17 | 5 | 85 |
| 20 –24 | 22 | 0 | 0 |
| **Total** | | $n = 30$ | $\sum (fx) = 265$ |

**Figure 2.2** Frequency of slope angles

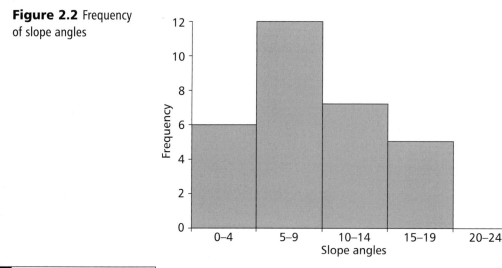

Average $= \Sigma fx/n = 265/30 = 8.81°$.

The **modal group** is the one which occurs with the most frequency, that is 5–9°. The **median** or middle value will be the average of the 15th and 16th values when ranked. These are both in the 5–9° group (**Figure 2.2**).

## Review

3 A survey of distances travelled by shoppers to a hypermarket is shown below.

| Distance (km) | Number of shoppers |
|---------------|--------------------|
| 0–2           | 16                 |
| 3–5           | 23                 |
| 6–10          | 12                 |
| 11–15         | 8                  |
| 16–20         | 1                  |

a Plot the data in the form of a bar chart (see **Chapter 5 section G**).
b Work out the average, modal group and median distance travelled by shoppers to the hypermarket.
c Which of these measures is (i) most and (ii) least satisfactory? Justify your choice.
d What conclusions do you draw from the data?

SECTION C

# Measures of dispersion

So far we have looked only at ways of summarising the data by showing some sort of 'average'. This is sometimes referred to as a measure of **central tendency**, giving one figure to describe a complete data set. However, it is often useful to show how far figures differ from the average. This measure is known as **dispersion**, and there are a number of ways of showing it.

The simplest is to use the **range** – the difference between the maximum (largest) and the minimum (smallest) values. This has its limitations, however, and is not great for data where there is considerable variation between records, as for example in the case of annual rainfall figures. An alternative measure is the **inter-quartile range**. This is similar to the range, but refers only to the middle half of the results. In other words, the extremes are omitted.

**Figure 2.3** Annual rainfall totals for Tel Aviv (mm), 1974–1993

| Year | Rainfall (mm) | Year | Rainfall (mm) | Year | Rainfall (mm) | Year | Rainfall (mm) |
|------|---------------|------|---------------|------|---------------|------|---------------|
| 1974 | 86  | 1979 | 192 | 1984 | 807 | 1989 | 195 |
| 1975 | 125 | 1980 | 418 | 1985 | 361 | 1990 | 274 |
| 1976 | 184 | 1981 | 80  | 1986 | 209 | 1991 | 148 |
| 1977 | 75  | 1982 | 361 | 1987 | 452 | 1992 | 390 |
| 1978 | 538 | 1983 | 460 | 1988 | 235 | 1993 | 84  |

Putting the data in **Figure 2.3** in order we get:

75, 80, 84, 86, 125, 148, 184, 192, 195, 209, 235, 274, 361, 361, 390, 418, 452, 460, 538, 807.

The maximum is 807mm, the minimum is 75mm and the range is thus from 807 to 75, that is 732mm.

The inter-quartile range is found by removing the top and bottom quarters and stating the range of values that remains. The intervals between quarters are **quartiles**; the value of the first quartile is termed $Q_1$, and the third quartile is $Q_3$. The inter-quartile range is $Q_3 - Q_1$. In the example above, this is quite easy to calculate, taking the fifth value ($Q_1$)(125) from the 15th value ($Q_3$)(390). Thus the inter-quartile range is $390 - 125 = 265$, a value which clearly gets rid of the extreme values and some of the spikiness in **Figure 2.4**.

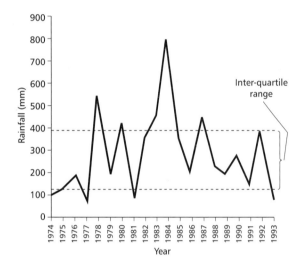

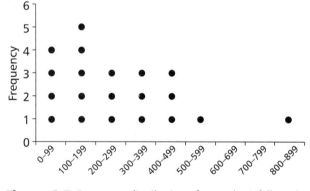

**Figure 2.5** Frequency distribution of annual rainfall totals for Tel Aviv, 1974–1993

**Figure 2.4** Line graph showing annual rainfall at Tel Aviv, 1974–93, with inter-quartile range indicated

## Review

4 The data below are annual rainfall records over the last 20 years for a site close to Oxford:
783, 509, 710, 577, 752, 634, 683, 655, 578, 608, 662, 704, 592, 571, 598, 473, 527, 796, 731, 699.

a   Illustrate the data by means of **(i)** a line graph (as **Figure 2.4**) and **(ii)** a frequency distribution (as **Figure 2.5**).
b   State **(i)** the maximum, **(ii)** the minimum, **(iii)** the range and **(iv)** the inter-quartile range of the rainfall for the 20-year period.
c   Which of these descriptive statistics is the best one in your opinion? Justify your answer.
d   Write a brief account pointing out the main features of the data.

Not every case is as easy! For example, there may be 21 or 22 values, rather than in this case where the number of observations (20) is readily divisible by 4. In those situations we have to make an informed guess at where the quartile would be. For instance, if we take the case of 21 observations, then the quartiles are at 51/4 and 163/4.

In the following example, with rainfall for 1994 (210mm) added to the 20 values we already have for Tel Aviv we can then make the estimate as shown below.

Set of values: 75, 80, 84, 86, 125, 148, 184, 192, 195, 209, 210, 235, 274, 361, 361, 390, 418, 452, 460, 538, 807.

The first quartile (51/4) lies a quarter of the way between 125 and 148, while the third quartile (163/4) lies three-quarters of the way between 361 and 390. Thus the first quartile is found by adding one quarter of the difference of 148 and 125 to 125, that is:

$$125 + \frac{(148-125)}{4} = 130.75.$$

The third quartile is found by adding three-quarters of the difference of 361 and 390 to 361, that is:

$$361 + 3\,\frac{(390-361)}{4} = 382.75.$$

Thus, the inter-quartile range is 382.75 – 130.75, i.e. 252.

In the next case there are 22 observations, as the data have been extended to include the rainfall total for 1995 (175mm):

75, 80, 84, 86, 125, 148, 175, 184, 192, 195, 209, 210, 235, 274, 361, 361, 390, 418, 452, 460, 538, 807.

The quartiles are now found at 5.5 and 16.5 (each quarter is 5.5 in size). Thus the first quartile is found half-way between the fifth and sixth figures, 125 and 148 (136.5) and the third quartile is found half-way between the 16th and 17th values, 361 and 390 (375.5). Thus the inter-quartile range in this case is 375.5 – 136.5 = 239mm.

In the final example, rainfall for 1996 (400mm) has been added, so there are now 23 observations:

75, 80, 84, 86, 125, 148, 175, 184, 192, 195, 209, 210, 235, 274, 361, 361, 390, 400, 418, 452, 460, 538, 807.

The procedure is as before. Given that there are 23 observations, the quartiles are now located every 5.75 readings (23 divided by 4). Thus the first quartile is found three-quarters of the way between the fifth value and the sixth, and the third quartile is found one-quarter of the way from the 17th value to the 18th. Thus, the first quartile is:

$$125 + 3\frac{(148 - 125)}{4} = 142.25$$

and the third quartile is:

$$390 + \frac{(400 - 390)}{4} = 392.5.$$

Thus the inter-quartile range in this case is 392.5 – 142.25 = 250.25.

## Moving means

**Moving means** are used to even out the fluctuations in values such as we have seen in the Tel Aviv rainfall figures. By so doing, trends may become more apparent.

With distributions such as annual rainfall values, it is customary to calculate five-year moving means. What happens is that the first five values in the sequence are added and then averaged – i.e. the total is divided by 5. The first value is then dropped from the data, the sixth added and the calculation of the mean is repeated. This sequence is repeated until the last of the values has been taken into account. The series of five-year moving means can then be plotted on a graph.

### Review

**5 a** Work out the five-year moving means for the Tel Aviv data given in **Figure 2.3**.
   **b** Graph your results.
   **c** What trends emerge, if any?
   **d** Compare your graph with **Figure 2.4**.

## Standard deviation

Another way of showing grouping around a central value is by using the **standard deviation**. This is one of the most important descriptive statistics, because it takes into account all the values in a distribution. This is necessary in testing for probability and for more complex inferential, explanatory statistics (see **Chapter 3 section A**).

Standard deviation measures the dispersal of figures around the mean, and is based on the idea of probability. It is calculated by first measuring the mean and then comparing the difference between each value and the mean. If a number of observations are made, we might expect:

- most values to be quite close to the average;
- a small number of very high or low values;
- equal numbers of values above and below the mean.

If we were to plot such a distribution on a graph (either in the form of a histogram or a continuous line graph), it would look something like **Figure 2.6**.

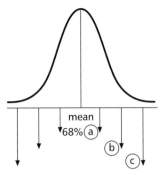

(a) 68% of the values lie within ±1 standard deviation of the mean

(b) 95% of the values lie within ±2 standard deviation of the mean

(c) 99% of the values lie within ±3 standard deviation of the mean

**Figure 2.6** A normal distribution curve

Figure 2.6 shows quite clearly all of the above points. The standard deviation is then a measure of the dispersion or variation around the mean. The formula for this is:

$$\text{standard deviation } (S \text{ or } s) = \sqrt{\frac{\Sigma \, (x - y)^2}{n}}$$

where $x$ refers to each observation, $y$ to the mean, $n$ to the number of points, and $(x - y)^2$ tells us to take the mean from each observation, and then to square the result. The following example shows the working out.

Annual rainfall totals for Tel Aviv: 86, 125, 184, 75, 538, 192, 418, 80, 361, 460, 807, 361, 209, 452, 235, 195, 274, 148, 390, 84.

First calculate the mean: $\dfrac{\Sigma(x)}{n} = \dfrac{5\ 674}{20} = 283.7$

Then construct a table as in **Figure 2.7** (although laborious, it is the way to make sure that you get it right).

| x | y | (x – y) | (x – y)² |
|---|---|---|---|
| 86 | 283.7 | −197.7 | 39 085.29 |
| 125 | 283.7 | −158.7 | 25 185.69 |
| 75 | 283.7 | −99.7 | 9 940.09 |
| 538 | 287.7 | −208.7 | 43 555.69 |
| 192 | 287.7 | 254.3 | 64 668.49 |
| 418 | 287.7 | −91.7 | 8 408.89 |
| 80 | 287.7 | 134.3 | 18 036.49 |
| 361 | 287.7 | 203.7 | 41 493.69 |
| 460 | 287.7 | 77.3 | 5 975.29 |
| 807 | 287.7 | 523.3 | 5 580.09 |
| 361 | 287.7 | 77.3 | 28 324.89 |
| 209 | 287.7 | −74.7 | 2 371.69 |
| 452 | 287.7 | 168.3 | 7 867.69 |
| 235 | 287.7 | −48.7 | 94.09 |
| 195 | 287.7 | −88.7 | 18 414.49 |
| 274 | 287.7 | −9.7 | 94.09 |
| 148 | 287.7 | −135.7 | 18 414.49 |
| 390 | 287.7 | 106.3 | 11 299.69 |
| 84 | 287.7 | −199.7 | 39 880.09 |
| Σ = 5 674 | | 0 | Σ=634 008.42 |

**Figure 2.7** Calculating the standard deviation

Thus, the standard deviation is found by putting the figures into the formula:

$$S(s) = \sqrt{\frac{634\,008.42}{20}} = \sqrt{31{,}700.42} = 178.05.$$

Thus the average deviation of all values around the mean (283.7mm) is 178.05mm. This gives a much more accurate figure than the range or the inter-quartile range, as it takes into account all values and is not as affected by extreme values. Given normal probability we would expect that about 68 per cent of the observations will fall within one standard deviation of the mean, about 95 per cent within two standard deviations of the mean, and about 99 per cent within three standard deviations.

## Review

6 The following data were collected on Shotover Hill, Oxford. The first two columns contain the slope angles (in degrees), recorded when measurements were taken every 5 metres up the slope. The second two columns show the results when measurements were taken every 10 metres.

| Slope angles (every 5 metres) | | | Slope angles (every 5 metres) | | | Slope angles (every 10 metres) | | | Slope angles (every 10 metres) | | |
|---|---|---|---|---|---|---|---|---|---|---|---|
| 5 | 4 | 5 | 11 | 11 | 2 | 9 | 8 | 10 | 7 | 6 | 5 |
| 9 | 5 | 10 | 13 | 9 | 4 | 15 | 15 | 13 | 3 | 9 | 9 |
| 17 | 7 | 12 | 12 | 9 | 4 | 7 | 5 | 3 | 10 | 10 | 6 |
| 22 | 19 | 12 | 14 | 12 | 6 | 1 | 3 | 5 | 7 | 8 | 8 |
| 19 | 10 | 10 | 15 | 8 | 10 | 3 | 5 | 5 | 8 | 5 | 8 |
| 15 | 11 | 8 | 13 | 6 | 12 | 5 | 7 | 6 | 4 | 3 | 3 |
| 10 | 11 | 8 | 12 | 2 | 19 | 5 | 3 | 9 | 2 | 2 | 4 |
| 7 | 11 | 10 | 10 | 4 | 21 | 9 | 10 | 10 | 5 | 7 | 8 |
| 5 | 13 | 12 | 10 | 9 | 22 | 6 | 7 | 8 | 10 | 17 | 20 |
| 2 | 12 | 8 | 11 | 17 | 16 | 8 | 8 | 5 | 19 | 8 | 3 |
| 4 | 14 | 11 | 9 | 19 | 12 | 8 | 4 | 3 | 16 | 10 | 9 |
| 5 | 15 | 16 | 9 | 15 | 10 | 2 | 2 | 9 | 11 | 13 | 9 |
| 7 | 13 | 21 | 12 | 10 | 8 | 8 | 10 | 15 | | | |
| 9 | 12 | 12 | 8 | 7 | 8 | 15 | 13 | 7 | | | |
| 10 | 10 | 7 | 6 | 5 | 7 | 5 | 3 | 1 | | | |
| 11 | 10 | 5 | 2 | 2 | 7 | 3 | 5 | 3 | | | |
| 11 | 11 | 1 | | | | 5 | 5 | 5 | | | |

**Figure 2.8** Slope measurements taken at Shotover Hill, Oxford

**a** Work out the mean, mode, median, maximum, minimum and range for the 5-metre data and 10-metre data.

**b** Work out the frequency of slopes in the following categories or groups:

| Slope angle | 0–4 | 5–9 | 10–14 | 15–19 | 20+ |
|---|---|---|---|---|---|
| Number of slopes (for both intervals) | * | * | * | * | * |

**c** Plot the data in the form of a histogram. This is simply a bar chart with classes or categories on the horizontal axis and frequencies on the vertical axis, as shown in **Figure 2.1**. Do this for both 5-metre and 10-metre samples, and then state which is the modal group in each case.

**d** Write a brief summary interpreting the results of your investigation.

# The location quotient

Somewhat different to the measures considered so far is the **location quotient**. It is an eminently geographical measure, in that it assesses the degree of concentration of any industry in a particular area. It is one of the most easily calculated descriptive statistics that is available, and is computed in the following way:

$$\frac{r/n}{R/N}$$

where $r$ is the number of people employed in industry $A$ in area $X$, $n$ is the number of people employed in area $X$, $R$ is the number of people employed nationally in industry $A$ and $N$ is the total number of people employed nationally.

For example, if there are 2 000 people employed in education in Oxford out of a total labour force of 40 000, compared with a national total of 200 000 employed in education and a total labour force of 20 000 000, the location quotient would be as follows:

$$\frac{2\ 000/40\ 000}{200\ 000/20\ 000\ 000} \quad = \quad \frac{0.05}{0.01} \quad = \quad 5$$

This means that the education sector in the Oxford area is over-represented by five times the national average. It would be concluded that education is of great significance to the local economy.

A location quotient of:

>1.0 reveals that a region has an above average representation of that particular industry;

1.0 shows that an area has the same representation as the national average (e.g. we would expect all areas to have roughly the same proportion of workers in services such as gas, electricity and refuse collection);

<1.0 reveals an under-representation of a particular industry.

## Review

7 Study the following data.

| Region | Metals | Machinery | Chemicals | Food |
|--------|--------|-----------|-----------|------|
| Keihin | 0.71 | 4.41 | 1.05 | 0.81 |
| Hanshin | 1.45 | 0.9 | 0.85 | 0.91 |
| Chukyo | 0.83 | 1.33 | 0.74 | 0.72 |
| N Kyushu | 1.66 | 0.5 | 0.81 | 1.41 |
| N Kanto | 1.06 | 1.22 | 0.55 | 0.89 |
| Keiyo | 1.66 | 0.41 | 2.49 | 1.04 |
| Tokai | 0.58 | 1.15 | 0.81 | 1.03 |
| Setouchi | 1.24 | 0.76 | 1.99 | 0.72 |

Location quotients for the major industrial regions of Japan

a Which of the four industries appears to be most evenly distributed between the regions? Justify your choice and suggest reasons for the evenness.

b Which of the four industries appears to be most unevenly distributed? Explain how you reach your conclusion and suggest reasons for the unevenness.

c On the basis of these four industries, which region do you think is the most important overall? Explain how you reach your conclusion.

d Which region shows the most balanced mix of industries? Explain how you reach your conclusion.

# Using spreadsheets

Given the computer hardware and software that is available in virtually all secondary schools today, it may be useful to say something about the use of spreadsheets in the handling and processing of statistics, both descriptive and inferential.

Here is an exercise to familiarise yourself with the spreadsheet function. The exact procedure may vary from computer to computer, or with software, but the general principles remain the same.

## Review

a  On the hard disk enter into your spreadsheet programme.

b  You should now be facing a screen with lots of blank rows and columns on it. Enter the following data, together with the necessary labels.

|   | A | B | C |
|---|---|---|---|
| **1** | **Site No.** | **Infiltration** | **Gradient** |
| **2** | 1 | 30 | 2 |
| **3** | 2 | 26 | 3 |
| **4** | 3 | 24 | 4 |
| **5** | 4 | 23 | 6 |
| **6** | 5 | 17 | 7 |
| **7** | 6 | 16 | 8 |
| **8** | 7 | 12 | 8 |

Survey data relating to infiltration and slope gradient

c  The spreadsheet allows us to enter formulae into boxes (cells) which will then compute the answers you require using the data we have already put in. For example, for the data on infiltration in cells B2 to B8, the following formulae are very useful:

- to find the sum, type =Sum (B2..B8);
- to find the average, type =Sum (B2..B8)/7;
- to multiply two values, type =B2*C2 (shift 8 =*);
- to divide one value by another, type =B2/C2;
- to find the standard deviation, type =STDEV (B2..B8);
- to find the square root, type =(B2^0.5) (shift 6 gives the square root function ^);
- to find the square of a box, type = B2*B2;
- to find the power 2/3 (for Manning's 'N'), type =(B2^0.66).

The sign = alerts the computer that a formula will be put in a cell (box) rather than a value. Once you press return or click on the tick at the screen the result will be automatically presented.

There is no need to type the formula into all the cells in a row or a column. All you need to do is :

- click on the cell containing the formula;
- holding the mouse down, drag across the row or column to select all the boxes;
- on the Calculate menu, choose Fill Right or Fill Down as appropriate. This transfers the formula to all the boxes in that row/column.

**SECTION H**

# Summing up

In this chapter, we have made the following major points.

- Numerical data can be of four types – nominal, ordinal, interval or ratio.
- There are two types of statistics – descriptive and inferential.
- Descriptive statistics seek to summarise numerical data, identifying the salient features of a series of values by such measures as the mean, range, mode, median and standard deviation.
- The last of these measure – standard deviation – makes two assumptions, namely that the laws of probability apply and that the data have a normal distribution. It is these two assumptions that underlie inferential statistics (see **Chapter 3**).
- The location quotient is a much-used measure in geographical investigations concerned with patterns of density and concentration.
- Spreadsheets are ideal in manipulating data and for undertaking recurrent calculations. Every A-level student should know how to use them.

# Inferential statistics

## Basic concepts

Inferential statistics use observations as a basis for making estimates or predictions. In other words, they make an inference about either a 'population' much larger than the one already observed or measured, or about a future situation. For example, let us assume that a survey has been carried out in your school to find out what percentage of students taking Geography at GCSE have opted to do the subject at A-level. Using that data, we may attempt to do two things:

- forecast how many of next year's GCSE Geography class in your school will opt to do A-level Geography;
- estimate how many students are taking A-level Geography in other schools within the same city (assuming we know how many took GCSE Geography).

To understand inferential statistics and their predictive abilities, it is vital to grasp three related concepts which are incorporated as assumptions: **probability**, **significance** and **sampling**.

## Probability

One of the main tasks of inferential statistics is to establish the likelihood of a particular event or value occurring – this is probability. Probability is measured on a scale running from 0 to 1. The value 1 represents absolute certainty – for instance, the likelihood or probability that you will one day die (**Figure 3.1**). The value 0 represents absolute impossibility – for example, the likelihood or probability that I might one day become President of the USA. If all things were as clear-cut as this, there would be no need for statisticians. But the truth of the matter is that many aspects of life involve probabilities that lie somewhere between 0 and 1.

In statistics, probability ($p$) is more often expressed as a percentage:

**Figure 3.1** Probability and significance scales

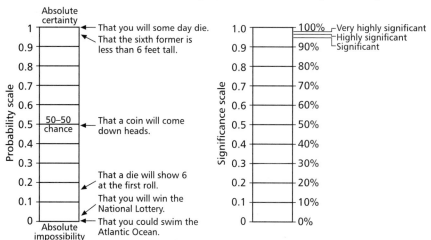

INFERENTIAL STATISTICS 21

- $p = 0.05$ (a 20 to 1 chance) is expressed as a 95 per cent level of probability;
- $p = 0.01$ (a 100 to 1 chance) is expressed as a 99 per cent level of probability;
- $p = 0.001$ (a 1 000 to 1 chance) is expressed as a 99.9 per cent level of probability.

## Sampling

Let us return to the example just mentioned of trying to predict how many GCSE students in the city as a whole will be taking A-level Geography. Clearly, it is necessary to establish how reliable our findings are, based on the initial survey of one class at one school. Put the other way round, how well does our sample class represent the whole of the city's population of GCSE students? What is the probability that our one-class sample is truly **representative** of (i.e. does not differ markedly from) all the GCSE classes in the city? To help us answer these questions, we turn to the concept of significance.

## Significance

Significance relates to the probability that a hypothesis is true. Let us take the **null hypothesis** – that there is no significant difference between the pattern of A-level choice at your school and that at another secondary school elsewhere in the same city. The probability at which it is decided to reject this null hypothesis is termed the **significance level**. The significance level indicates the number of times that the observed difference (as between the two schools) could be expected to occur by chance. The practice is to refer to results as 'significant', 'highly significant' or 'very highly significant' respectively when significant at the 5 per cent (95 per cent), 1 per cent (99 per cent) or 0.1 per cent (99.9 per cent) levels (**Figure 3.1**). This means that there is respectively a 1 in 20, 1 in 100 or 1 in 1 000 probability of the given result occurring (or, conversely, not occurring) by chance.

Having clarified these basic concepts, let us now look at some of the techniques of inferential statistics. The first relates to the second of the concepts.

### Review

1 Explain and illustrate the difference between descriptive and inferential statistics.

2 Define each of the following and explain why it is important in inferential statistics:
   a probability;
   b significance;
   c sampling.

3 Explain why a 99 per cent probability is a 100 to 1 chance.

**SECTION B**

# Sampling error or standard error

This statistic gives an estimate of the true 'population' mean, namely the value we would get were it possible to measure everything (i.e. visit all the schools). It is based on two assumptions: probability theory and the normal distribution (**Chapter 2 section E**). We expect that in a series of measurements or values, there will be very few very large values, very few very small values and that the majority of the values will tend to occur around the mean. So, any estimate that we might arrive at is probably going to be quite close to the true population mean. Our estimates are unlikely to be much larger or much smaller than than the true mean. Thus, it is possible to estimate within certain limits where the true population mean lies. The following example illustrates the point.

For example, in a survey of vegetation characteristics on the Isle of Purbeck, a sample of 100 points found that 50 per cent of the area was farmland, 14 per cent heathland, 12 per cent woodland and 24 per cent other. From these figures it is possible to state that the true population mean for woodland is somewhere around 12 per cent. The formula for the sampling or standard error is $\sqrt{P\,(100-p)/n}$, where $P$ refers to the proportion of woodland, $(100-p)$ is the proportion that is not woodland (i.e. in this case farmland, heathland and other) and $n$ is the sample size. The formula gives us the limits to the mean.

Thus our estimate of the proportion of woodland that exists on the Isle of Purbeck becomes

$$12\% \pm \sqrt{12 \times 88/100} = 12\% \pm 3.2\% = \text{from 8.8\% to 15.2\%.}$$

We are saying therefore that we know that our own survey may not be totally accurate and that the true population mean is likely to lie somewhere between these limits.

The larger the sample size the more accurate the estimate. In the above example, if the proportion of woodland were still 12 per cent but the sample size was 1 000, the standard error or sampling error would be $12\% \pm \sqrt{12 \times 88/1000} = 12\% \pm 1.0\%$.

Equally, given the results from our sample of 100 we could say that:

- one standard error = $12\% \pm 3.2\%$, = 8.8–15.2%;
- two standard errors = $12\% \pm 6.4\% = 5.6$–18.4%;
- three standard errors = $12\% \pm 9.6\% = 2.4$–21.6.3%.

**Figure 3.2** Vegetation survey in the Vale of the White Horse

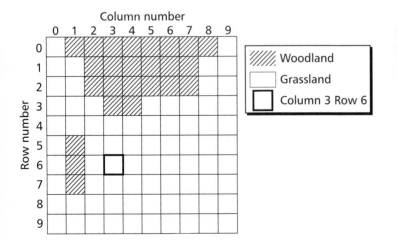

## Review

4 **Figure 3.2** shows the distribution of grassland and woodland in the vicinity of the Vale of the White Horse, Oxfordshire.
  a For the area as a whole, calculate the ratio of grassland to woodland.
  b Calculate the ratio of grassland to woodland i) in column 9 and ii) in row 1.

c Out of a sample of 25 squares, it has been found that in the first 15, four squares are woodland and 11 are grassland. Check the vegetation of the rest of the sample, from the following random numbers drawn from the random number table (see **Appendix**, Table 3): 36 (i.e. column 3, row 6 – grassland), 81, 03, 76, 53, 65, 59, 18, 00, 90.

d Estimate the percentage of the area that is grassland.

e Using the formula for sampling error ($\sqrt{P\,(P-100)/n}$), work out the limits for the true population mean, based on the sample of 25 points.

f What would the limits be if the sample size had been 100? (Substitute 100 for 25 in the equation.)

g What does this suggest to you about sample size and the degree of accuracy about population means?

**SECTION C**

# Confidence limits

Still on the subject of the degree to which we can rely on the results of a sample survey, let us briefly move on to what are called **confidence limits**. Confidence limits are more widely used in the present context than the number of standard errors. They are based on probability, and assume that the data being sampled have a normal distribution (**Figure 2.6**).

Confidence limits are usually established at the 68 per cent, 95 per cent and 99 per cent levels. These limits are found by multiplying the standard error by 1, 1.96 and 2.58 respectively. The multipliers are in fact standard deviations (**Figure 2.6**).

## Case Study

Let us return to the results of the land use survey on the Isle of Purbeck. The percentage figure for woodland was 12 per cent and the standard error was calculated as 3.2 per cent. So at the 95 per cent confidence level, the actual confidence limits for woodland would be:

$$12\% \pm (3.2 \times 1.96) = 12\% \pm 6.27 = \text{from } 18.27\% \text{ to } 5.63\%.$$

At the 99 per cent confidence level, the limits would be:

$$12\% \pm (3.2 \times 2.56) = 12\% \pm 8.19 = \text{from } 20.19\% \text{ to } 3.81\%.$$

From this it follows that at the 68 per cent level, the limits would be $12\% \pm 3.2 \times 1 = \text{from } 15.2 \text{ per cent to } 8.8 \text{ per cent}$.

We may express all this in a slightly different way and say that if the actual woodland mean was 12 per cent (if every piece of land use were recorded), then we would expect that:

**Review**

**5** Using the values that you have calculated in parts **d** and **e** of **Review question 4** above, work out the limits at the 95 per cent confidence level.

- 68 per cent of surveys would record the mean as lying between 8.8 per cent and 15.2 per cent;
- 95 per cent of surveys would record the mean as lying between 5.63 per cent and 18.27 per cent;
- 99 per cent of surveys would record the mean as lying between 3.81 per cent and 20.19 per cent.

We return to this issue of confidence limits in **Chapter 6 section A**.

SECTION D

# Spearman's rank correlation coefficient (*Rs*)

## Correlation

Testing for **correlation** is a common task in geographical investigations. Correlation is the degree of relationship between pairs of variables. When the two variables (for instance, town size and the number of shops) increase or decrease together, the relationship is known as **positive correlation**. With **negative correlation**, there is an inverse relationship, so that as one variable increases (say slope angle) the other decreases (say percolation). A correlation coefficient is an index or measure giving a precise value to the linear relationship between two or more variables. Values range from +1.0 (perfect positive correlation) to −1.0 (perfect negative correlation). If the relationship between the variables is a random one, the coefficient value will be 0, or nearly so. Significance levels crop up here, for as elsewhere geographers use the 95 per cent and 99 per cent levels of significance. This means that when they say a significant correlation exists, they are at least 95 per cent sure that they are right! There is only a 1 in 20 chance that the correlation is due to chance.

Spearman's rank correlation coefficient is one of the most widely used statistics in geography. It is relatively quick and easy to calculate. It only requires that data are available on the ordinal (ranked) scale, although other data can be transformed into ranks very simply. It is called a 'rank' correlation because only the ranks are correlated, not the actual values. In some cases, it is obvious whether a correlation exists or not. However, in most cases it is not so clear-cut, and to avoid subjective comments we use *Rs* to bring in a degree of statistical accuracy. The coefficient scale runs from +1.0 to -1.0 (**Figure 3.3**).

**Figure 3.3** Some Spearman's rank correlation coefficients

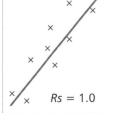

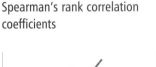

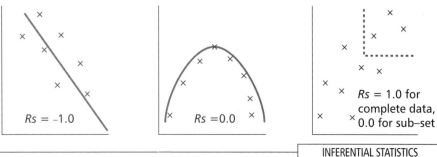

| Sample | Organic content (%) | Moisture content (%) | Sample | Organic content (%) | Moisture content (%) |
|--------|---------------------|----------------------|--------|---------------------|----------------------|
| 1 | 3.8 | 15 | 6 | 7.1 | 29 |
| 2 | 4.7 | 22 | 7 | 6.2 | 26 |
| 3 | 6.2 | 30 | 8 | 4.6 | 20 |
| 4 | 3.9 | 18 | 9 | 4.6 | 25 |
| 5 | 5.4 | 24 | 10 | 5.1 | 20 |

**Figure 3.4** Samples of soil organic and moisture content

## Procedure

a State the null hypothesis ($H_0$) that is there is no significant relationship between organic content and moisture content. The alternative hypothesis ($H_1$) is that there is a significant relationship between the two variables.

b Rank both sets of data in **Figure 3.4** from high to low so that the highest value gets rank 1, second highest 2, and so on (**Figure 3.5**). In the case of joint ranks find the average rank. For example, if two similar values occupy positions two and three, they both take on rank 2.5; if three similar values occupy positions four, five and six, they all take rank 5.

c Using the formula $Rs = 1 - \dfrac{6\Sigma d^2}{n^3 - n}$ work out the correlation, where $d$ refers to the difference between ranks and $n$ the number of observations.

**Figure 3.5** Stages in the calculation of the Spearman's rank correlation coefficient

d Compare the computed $Rs$ with the critical significance level values in **Appendix Table 1**.

## Worked example

| Sample | Organic content (%) | Moisture content (%) | Organic content rank | Moisture content rank | $d$ | $d^2$ |
|--------|---------------------|----------------------|----------------------|-----------------------|-----|-------|
| 1 | 3.8 | 15 | 10 | 10 | 0 | 0 |
| 2 | 4.7 | 22 | 6 | 6 | 0 | 0 |
| 3 | 6.2 | 30 | 2.5 | 1 | 1.5 | 2.25 |
| 4 | 3.9 | 18 | 9 | 9 | 0 | 0 |
| 5 | 5.4 | 24 | 4 | 5 | −1 | 1 |
| 6 | 7.1 | 29 | 1 | 2 | −1 | 1 |
| 7 | 6.2 | 26 | 2.5 | 3 | −0.5 | 0.25 |
| 8 | 4.6 | 20 | 7.5 | 7.5 | 0 | 0 |
| 9 | 4.6 | 25 | 7.5 | 4 | 3.5 | 10.25 |
| 10 | 5.1 | 20 | 5 | 7.5 | −2.5 | 6.25 |
|  |  |  |  |  |  | $\Sigma d^2 = 21$ |

$$Rs = 1 - \frac{6\Sigma d^2}{n^3 - n} = 1 - \frac{6 \times 21}{10^3 - 10} = 1 - \frac{126}{990} = 1 - 0.13 = 0.87.$$

Once the value of the coefficient (Rs) has been computed, it is compared with the critical values. For a sample of ten, the critical values are 0.564 for the 95 per cent significance level and 0.746 for the 99 per cent significance level (**Appendix Table 1**). In this example, therefore, it is clear that the relationship is very strong. There is a more than 99 per cent probability that there is a relationship between the data. The next stage would be to offer explanations for the relationship.

It is important to realise that Spearman's coefficient has its weaknesses and to bear these in mind.

- It requires a sample of not less than seven observations.
- It tests for linear relationships, and would give an answer of 0 for data such as river discharge and frequency which follow a curvilinear pattern, with few very low or very high flows and a large number of medium flows (**Figure 3.3**).
- It is easy to make meaningless correlations – for instance, between factory size and height above sea-level.
- The question of scale is always important. As shown on the final diagram of **Figure 3.3**, an analysis of river sediment rates and discharge for the whole of a drainage system may give a strong correlation, whereas analysis of just the upper catchment might give a much lower result.

As always, statistics are tools to be used. They are only part of the analysis; we must be aware of their limits at all times.

## Review

6 Identify the nature of each of the four correlations shown in **Figure 3.3**.
7 Refer to the following data on slope angle and soil depth:

| Slope angle(°) | Soil depth(cm) | Slope angle(°) | Soil depth(cm) | Survey data on slope angle and soil depth |
|---|---|---|---|---|
| 5.5 | 60 | 22 | 29 | |
| 11.5 | 48 | 18 | 24 | |
| 12 | 33 | 26 | 24 | |
| 13 | 18 | 20 | 12 | |
| 25 | 22 | 3 | 60 | |

a  State the null hypothesis.
b  Set out the data in a table as shown in the worked example, above.
c  Rank both sets of data from high to low (highest = rank 1).
d  Work out the difference in ranks.
e  Find the square of the differences.
f  Total the figures in the final column to find $\Sigma d^2$.
g  Using this figure work out the correlation coefficient between slope angle and soil depth.
h  Compare your answer with the critical values in the table. How significant is your result?
i  What conclusions do you draw about the possible relationship between slope angle and soil depth?
j  Suggest reasons for that relationship.

# Nearest-neighbour analysis

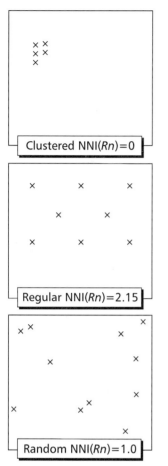

Figure 3.6  Different types of spatial pattern

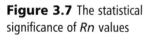

Much of Geography is concerned with distributions in space. Some of the most important distributions that we have to consider include rural settlements and the functions in urban areas. The spatial distribution of settlements in an area can be described by looking at a map. This may lead us to conclude that the settlements are scattered, dispersed or concentrated. However, the main weakness with the visual method is that it is subjective, and individuals differ in their interpretations of patterns. Some objective measure is required, and this is provided by the nearest-neighbour analysis.

Three main types of spatial pattern can be distinguished: uniform or regular, clustered or aggregated, and random (**Figure 3.6**). The points may represent settlements or indeed any feature which can be regarded as being located at a specific point, such as shops, factories, trees, etc. If the pattern is regular, the distance between any one point and its nearest neighbour should be approximately the same as from any other point. If the pattern is clustered then many points will be found a short distance from each other and there will be large areas of the map without any points. A random distribution normally has a mixture of some clustering and some regularity.

The technique most commonly used to identify the character of spatial patterns is nearest-neighbour analysis. The nearest-neighbour index ($Rn$) is derived by averaging the distance between each point and its nearest neighbour. This index can range in value between 0 and 2.15, where 0 indicates a highly clustered pattern and 2.15 a pattern that is regular. A value around 1 suggests that the pattern is essentially a random one (**Figure 3.7**).

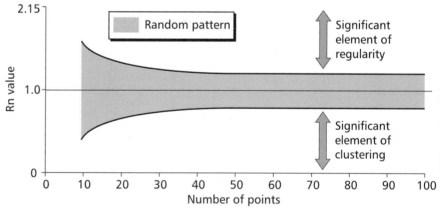

**Figure 3.7** The statistical significance of $Rn$ values

The formula for working out the nearest-neighbour index ($Rn$) is:

$$Rn = 2\overline{D} \ \sqrt{(n/a)}$$

where $\overline{D}$ is the average distance between each point and its nearest neighbour ($\Sigma d/n$), $n$ the number of points under study, and $a$ the size of the area under study. It is important that you use the same units for both distance and area e.g. metres or km, but not a mixture.

For example, a survey of the nine villages of Otmoor, in Oxfordshire, produced the following results.

| Village | Nearest neighbour (km) |
|---------|:----------------------:|
| Fencott | 1.5 |
| Noke | 2.0 |
| Islip | 2.0 |
| Horton | 3.0 |
| Beckley | 3.0 |
| Murcott | 1.0 |
| Merton | 1.0 |
| Oddington | 1.0 |
| Charlton | 1.5 |
| Elsfield | 2.0 |
| Woodeaton | 2.0 |
| | $\Sigma d = 20.5$ |

$$Rn = 2\overline{D}\,\sqrt{(n/a)} = 2 \times 20.5/11 \times \sqrt{(11/64)} = 2 \times 1.9 \times 0.414 = 1.57.$$

The $Rn$ value suggests a significant degree of clustering, even allowing for the small number of points involved in the survey (**Figure 3.7**).

**Figure 3.8** Patterns and their nearest-neighbour index values

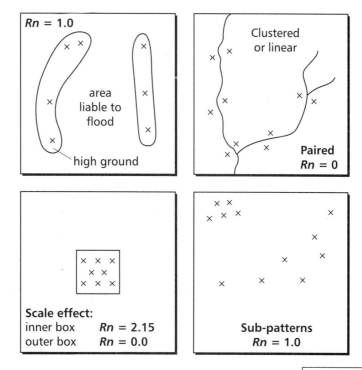

There are some important points to bear in mind when using nearest-neighbour analysis, particularly where settlement patterns are concerned.

- From where do you measure – the centre or edge of a settlement?
- Do you measure straight line distance, or the distance by road (or waterway)?
- What constitutes a settlement – individual houses, or a cluster involving more than a prescribed number of dwellings?
- Why do we take the nearest neighbour? Why not the second, third or fourth nearest?
- What is the effect of paired distributions (**Figure 3.8**)?
- One overall index may obliterate important sub-patterns (**Figure 3.8**).
- The choice of the area, and the size of the area studied, can completely alter the result and make a clustered pattern appear regular, and vice-versa (**Figure 3.8**).
- Although the nearest-neighbour index may suggest a random pattern, it may be that the controlling factor, for example soil type or altitude, is itself randomly distributed, and that the settlements are in fact located in anything but a random fashion.

## Review

8 The diagram below shows the distribution of shops and post boxes in part of a city centre.

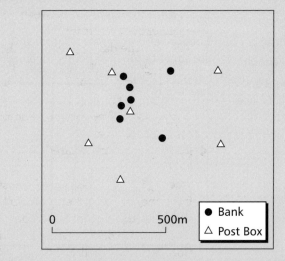

a Label both sets of points A to G.
b Measure the distance from each point to its nearest neighbour.
c Arrange these values in table form, as on p. 29.
d Calculate the nearest-neighbour index ($Rn$) for banks and post boxes ($n = 7$, $a = 1$ km$^2$ or 1,000,000m$^2$).
e What do the answers tell you about the distribution patterns of banks and post boxes?
f Suggest reasons for the differences.

# The chi-squared test

The chi-squared ($\chi^2$) test is one of the most widely-used and versatile tests of association. It is mainly used in the comparison of two frequency distributions, or to determine whether the observed frequencies ($O$) of a given phenomenon differ significantly from the frequencies that might be expected ($E$) according to some assumed hypothesis. It might be used, for example, to test for possible association between altitude and the frequency of cirques, or between levels of well-being and different sectors of a city.

The chi-squared test can only be used on data which have the following characteristics.

- The data must be in the form of frequencies.
- The frequency data must have a precise numerical value but must be organised into categories or groups.
- The total number of observations must be greater than twenty.
- The expected frequency in any one category must be greater than 5.

## Method

a State the hypothesis being tested. We might be keen to discover whether there is any association or relationship between the frequency of shops and distance from the city centre. Rather than pose it in a positive form, it is customary to state the possible association in the form of a null hypothesis (a negative test), namely that there is no significant difference between our two samples – one of shops and the other of distance from the city centre.

b Tabulate the data as shown in the example below. The value being tested for significance is known as the **observed frequency** ($O$) – e.g. the number of shops found in each of a series of distance bands from the city centre.

c Calculate the frequency (of shops) that you would expect to find ($E$) in each distance band.

d Calculate the chi-squared statistic using the formula:
$$\chi^2 = \Sigma(O - E)^2/E,$$
where $\chi^2$ is the chi-squared statistic, $\Sigma$ is the sum of, $O$ is the observed frequency and $E$ the expected frequency.

e Calculate the degrees of freedom. This is quite simply one less than the total number of observations ($n$), i.e. $n - 1$.

f Compare the calculated figure with the critical values in the significance tables (**Appendix Table 2**) using the appropriate degrees of freedom. Read off the probability that the data frequencies you have tested could have occurred by chance.

**Figure 3.9** provides data on the number of cirques in a defined area and their orientation. What is the probability that the number of cirques is related to orientation?

The null hypothesis ($H_0$) states that there is no significant variation in the frequency of cirques with orientation. The alternative hypothesis ($H_1$) would state that there is a significant difference in the frequency of cirques and orientation.

If there is no difference in the frequency of cirques, all orientations should show roughly the same frequency of cirques. That means they will all have the about the average. The expected frequency is thus the same as the average frequency, which is $(40 + 15 + 5 + 12)/4 = 72/4 = 18$.

| Orientation | No. of cirques |
|:-----------:|:--------------:|
| NE | 40 |
| SE | 15 |
| SW | 5 |
| NW | 12 |

**Figure 3.9** The orientation of cirques

| Orientation | No. of cirques (O) | Expected frequency(E) | (O–E) | (O–E)² | (O–E)²/E |
|:-----------:|:------------------:|:---------------------:|:-----:|:------:|:--------:|
| NE | 40 | 18 | 22 | 484 | 26.89 |
| SE | 15 | 18 | 3 | 9 | 0.5 |
| SW | 5 | 18 | 13 | 169 | 9.39 |
| NW | 12 | 18 | 6 | 36 | 2 |
| | | | | | Σ38.78 |

**Figure 3.10** Calculating chi-squared

Degrees of freedom (df) = $(n - 1) = (4 - 1) = 3$. The critical values for 3 df are:

| 0.10 | 0.05 | 0.01 | 0.001 |
|------|------|------|-------|
| 6.25 | 7.82 | 11.34 | 16.27 |

Clearly the computed value of 38.78 exceeds the critical values even at the 0.001 level of significance. This means that there is less than a one in a thousand (0.001) chance that there is no variation in the frequency of cirques and orientation. Therefore we would reject the null hypothesis and accept the alternative hypothesis. This means that there is a significant difference in (or association between) the frequency of cirques and their orientation.

The next stage in such an investigation would be to offer explanations for the results. Remember the statistic is only used as a means of clarification. It is not an end in itself, but simply a means to help you to explain.

Sometimes we know a lot of local detail. For example, we may know that in a given area:

- 10 per cent of the land is above 1 100m;
- 20 per cent of the land is between 900m and 1 100m;
- 30 per cent of the land is between 700m and 900m;
- 40 per cent of the land is between 500m and 700m.

| Altitude (m) | No. of cirques |
|---|---|
| >1 100 | 36 |
| 900–1 100 | 18 |
| 700–899 | 11 |
| 500–699 | 5 |
| Total | 70 |

**Figure 3.11** The altitudinal frequency of cirques

In this case, if there were no variation in the frequency of cirques and altitude, we would expect to find 10 per cent of cirques above 1,100m, 20 per cent between 900m and 1,100m, 30 per cent between 700m and 900m and 40 per cent between 500m and 700m. In a survey, the following results were obtained:

The total number observed at each level is the observed frequency (O). Due to the relative amount of land at different altitudinal bands, the expected will be 10 per cent of the observed total for the >1 000m group, 20 per cent for the 900–1 100m group, 30 per cent for the 700–899m group and 40 per cent for the 500–699m group.

## Review

9 Refer to the data in **Figure 3.11**.

   a What is the probability that there is a relationship between the number of cirques and altitude?

   b State the null hypothesis.

   c Work out the expected frequency for each altitude group.

   d Work out the $\chi^2$ statistic.

   e How significant is this?

   f Explain the reasons why there should be a relationship between altitude and the number of cirques.

## Chi-squared testing when there are more than two samples

It is much more usual that you will be looking at data which fall into a number of categories, rather than as shown above, which is the simplest case. The formula is the same, but the means of finding the expected values and the degrees of freedom differ. An example should clarify all of the points.

**Figure 3.12** Results of a survey of fields by land use and rock type

| Rock type | Arable | Pasture | Mixed |
|---|---|---|---|
| Limestone | 6 | 14 | 5 |
| Clay | 19 | 7 | 6 |
| Chalk | 5 | 12 | 5 |
| Granite | 7 | 7 | 7 |

The data in **Figure 3.12** refer to the number of fields in a region which are given over to different types of land use. The underlying geology is also given.

Null hypothesis: there is no variation in land use with respect to the different rock types.

Find the expected values if there were an equal proportion of each type of land use on each rock type. For this you need the formula:

$$E = \Sigma r \ \Sigma k / n$$

where $\Sigma r$ is the sum of each individual row, $\Sigma k$ is the sum of each individual column, and n is the total number of observations.

| Rock type | Arable | Pasture | Mixed | $\Sigma r$ |
|---|---|---|---|---|
| Limestone | 6 | 14 | 5 | 25 |
| Clay | 19 | 7 | 6 | 32 |
| Chalk | 5 | 12 | 5 | 22 |
| Granite | 7 | 7 | 7 | 21 |
| $\Sigma k$ | 37 | 40 | 23 | 100 |

To find the expected values, multiply the row total by the column total and divide by $n$.

| Rock type | Arable | Pasture | Mixed |
|---|---|---|---|
| Limestone | 37×25/100=9.25 | 40×25/100=10.0 | 23×25/100=5.75 |
| Clay | 37×32/100=11.8 | 40×32/100=12.8 | 23×32/100=7.4 |
| Chalk | 37×22/100=8.1 | 40×22/100=8.8 | 23×22/100=5.1 |
| Granite | 37×21/100=7.8 | 40×21/100=8.4 | 23×21/100=4.8 |

We can now continue to work out the $\chi^2$, given that we have O and also E.

| Rock type /land use | Observed frequency (O) | Expected frequency(E) | (O–E) | (O–E)$^2$ | (O–E)$^2$/E |
|---|---|---|---|---|---|
| L/A | 6 | 9.25 | –3.25 | 10.56 | 1.1 |
| L/P | 14 | 10 | 4 | 16 | 1.6 |
| L/M | 5 | 5.75 | –0.75 | 0.56 | 0.1 |
| Cl/A | 19 | 11.8 | 7.2 | 51.84 | 4.4 |
| Cl/P | 7 | 12.8 | –5.8 | 33.64 | 2.6 |
| Cl/M | 6 | 7.4 | –1.4 | 1.96 | 0.3 |
| Ch/A | 5 | 8.1 | –3.1 | 9.61 | 1.2 |
| Ch/P | 12 | 8.8 | 3.2 | 10.24 | 1.2 |
| Ch/M | 5 | 5.1 | –0.1 | 0.01 | 0.1 |
| G/A | 7 | 7.8 | –0.8 | 0.64 | 0.1 |
| G/P | 7 | 8.4 | –1.4 | 1.96 | 0.2 |
| G/M | 7 | 4.8 | 3.2 | 10.24 | 2.1 |
| | | | | | $\Sigma$15.0 |

Now calculate the degrees of freedom (df): in this sort of chi-squared test where there are more than two categories, we use the formula:

$$df = (r - 1) \times (k - 1),$$

where r and k refer to the number of rows and columns respectively. Thus, in this example, $df = (4 - 1) \times (3 - 1) = 3 \times 2 = 6$.

Compare the computed chi-squared statistic against the critical values in **Appendix Table 2**. For six degrees of freedom, the values are:

| 0.10 | 0.05 | 0.01 | 0.001 |
|------|------|------|-------|
| 10.6 | 12.6 | 16.8 | 22.5 |

Thus, we can say that the probability of there being no relationship between rock type and agricultural activity (i.e. the null hypothesis) is between 0.05 and 0.01, i.e. in only 5 to 1 per cent of cases. Thus we would reject the null hypothesis and accept the alternative hypothesis, namely that there is a relationship between rock type and agricultural activity. The next stage is, of course, to explain the relationship.

## SECTION G

# Summing up

In this chapter we have examined a selection of techniques that fall under the heading of inferential statistics. Inferential statistics are amongst the most widely used in A-level Geography, particularly in the individual project. The techniques are largely to do with probabilities and establishing whether or not there are significant relationships or associations between different data samples. They do not explain relationships or associations; they merely draw our attention to their existence should they be present. In order to use these techniques appropriately and to interpret results correctly, it is vital to have a sound grasp of the three concepts of probability, sampling and significance.

# Cartographic techniques

Perhaps of all the skills that we look at in this book, that of representing data or information in map form is the most geographical. Maps are drawn to show how things occur spatially. Much of Geography is about the description and explanation of spatial distributions as part of the variable character of the Earth's surface. A whole range of methods is available, but given the constraints of space only the more commonly used will be considered in this chapter.

A number of exercises will be set during this chapter, based on the city of Oxford (**Figure 4.1**). For these we shall use data contained in **Figures 4.2** and **4.3**. The outline map in **Figure 4.1** will be required for mapping selected aspects of this information.

**Figure 4.1** Outline map of Oxford wards

**Figure 4.2** Social and economic data for the wards of Oxford

| A | B | C | D | E | F | G |
|---|---|---|---|---|---|---|
| Wards | Pop. density (p/km²) | Unemployment | Households | Households | | |
| | | | | White | Afro-Carib | Asian |
| Blackbird Leys | 2,392 | 9.6% | 3,039 | 2,763 | 235 | 18 |
| Central | 320 | 2.3% | 286 | 262 | 2 | 11 |
| Cherwell | 1,768 | 4.0% | 2,836 | 2,688 | 34 | 35 |
| East | 2,852 | 6.9% | 2,672 | 2,370 | 80 | 152 |
| Headington | 2,575 | 5.9% | 2,836 | 2,733 | 68 | 26 |
| Iffley | 3,290 | 5.2% | 3,106 | 2,947 | 63 | 67 |
| Littlemore | 3,733 | 5.8% | 2,752 | 2,639 | 51 | 37 |
| Marston Parish | 1,888 | 4.1% | 1,263 | 1,289 | 8 | 11 |
| Marston Ward | 2,260 | 3.9% | 2,512 | 2,386 | 30 | 47 |
| North | 1,595 | 3.4% | 1,947 | 1,851 | 9 | 19 |
| Quarry | 3,466 | 4.3% | 2,623 | 2,505 | 30 | 33 |
| Risinghurst | 2,084 | 4.3% | 1,159 | 1,118 | 15 | 6 |
| South | 2,355 | 6.7% | 2,763 | 2,589 | 62 | 112 |
| St Clements | 3,195 | 8.0% | 3,116 | 2,746 | 86 | 190 |
| Temple Cowley | 2,380 | 5.5% | 2,547 | 2,350 | 84 | 76 |
| West | 1,553 | 5.5% | 2,657 | 2,512 | 35 | 56 |
| Wolvercote | 1,775 | 3.8% | 2,867 | 2,717 | 29 | 33 |
| Wood Farm | 2,482 | 5.0% | 2,711 | 2,591 | 52 | 28 |
| Oxford | 2,158 | 5.6% | 43 692 | 41 056 | 973 | 924 |

| A | B | C | D | E | F |
|---|---|---|---|---|---|
| Wards | Total crime | Crime per 1000 people | Burglary per 1000 people | Shoplifting per 1000 people | Car thefts per 1000 people |
| Blackbird Leys | 1,467 | 177 | 21 | 4 | 47 |
| Central | 4,671 | 7,298 | 308 | 1,682 | 993 |
| Cherwell | 752 | 106 | 15 | 4 | 25 |
| East | 1,093 | 154 | 37 | 14 | 39 |
| Headington | 1,179 | 153 | 24 | 1 | 60 |
| Iffley | 1,318 | 161 | 22 | 0 | 36 |
| Littlemore | 811 | 108 | 11 | 2 | 30 |
| Marston Parish | 495 | 150 | 14 | 2 | 27 |
| Marston Ward | 957 | 141 | 31 | 2 | 50 |
| North | 1,706 | 155 | 46 | 1 | 125 |
| Quarry | 2,005 | 291 | 33 | 1 | 146 |
| Risinghurst | 295 | 95 | 21 | 7 | 41 |
| South | 885 | 125 | 16 | 5 | 50 |
| St Clements | 2,185 | 297 | 46 | 2 | 66 |
| Temple Cowley | 1,078 | 152 | 23 | 32 | 42 |
| West | 775 | 168 | 15 | 4 | 32 |
| Wolvercote | 978 | 138 | 20 | 2 | 48 |
| Wood Farm | 758 | 101 | 11 | 1 | 38 |
| Oxford | 23,408 | 213 | 41.6 | 11 | 59 |

**Figure 4.3** Crime data for the wards of Oxford

# Dot maps

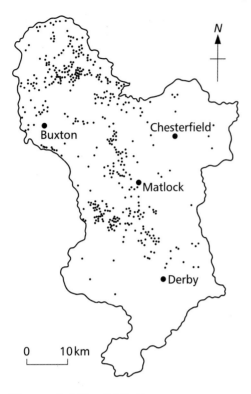

**Figure 4.4** The distribution of landslides in Derbyshire

Perhaps one of the simplest forms of distribution map is the **dot map (Figure 4.4)**. It can be used quite effectively to show a whole range of **point-located** data, from farms to factories, from landslides to leisure centres, from wells to weather stations.

Certainly a well-drawn dot map can give a good visual impression of a distribution, but there are some snags:

- they often need accurate location detail;
- they can be quite time-consuming to plot;
- all data points are assumed to be equal.

The last of these points is potentially serious, for quite clearly things like factories and farms can vary in size. The problem might be resolved by using dots of more than one size. In the plotting of factories, for example, you might use differently sized dots to distinguish say four categories on the basis of either floor space or labour force.

It goes almost without saying that symbols other than dots might be used in the construction of such simple distribution maps. Indeed, by using a range of symbols it is possible to show more than one distribution on the same map. The composite picture can often reveal interesting relationships, associations and patterns (**Figure 4.5**).

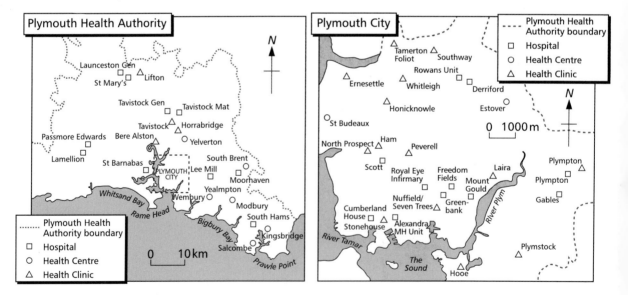

**Figure 4.5** Health facilities within the Plymouth Health Authority

## Review

1   For which of the following distributions do you think the dot method would be the most appropriate form of representation on a map:
    ■  volcanoes in the Northern Hemisphere;
    ■  population in a rural parish;
    ■  cities in England and Wales;
    ■  shops in a town;
    ■  outbreaks of cholera in India?
    Justify your choice by references to all five contenders.

2   Assume you are investigating the distribution of landslides in Derbyshire. What other distribution maps would you need besides **Figure 4.4**?

3   Write a short account pointing out the strengths and weaknesses of **Figure 4.5**.

## SECTION B

# Proportional symbols

**Figure 4.6** Tourism in the Caribbean

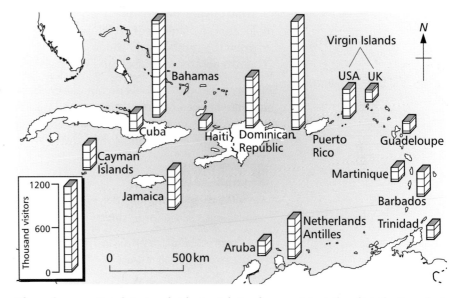

If you have point data to plot but wish to show not just the distribution, but also spatial variations in values, then proportional symbols may be suitable. At the basic level, the values might be represented as simple linear bars (**Figure 4.6**). However, it is more common to have the actual values represented by symbol area, rather than length. To do this, it is necessary to take the square root of the value that is to be represented as a basis for constructing the symbol. So in the case of proportional circles, that square root value determines the radius (**Figure 4.7**). With squares, it is the sides that are proportional to the square root.

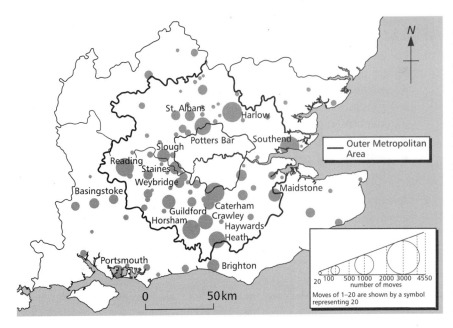

**Figure 4.7** Destinations of office moves in South-east England

Another critical step in using the technique is to arrive at a suitable scale (i.e. the ratio between units of value and units of radius). Identifying the lowest and highest values to be represented is important here. We need to be sure that the smallest circle or square is big enough to be seen, but also that the largest does not swamp the map.

So the steps in constructing proportional circles or squares are:

a calculate the square roots of the values to be represented;
b rank the square root values to determine the range;
c determine a scale that suits the range of square root values and the scale of your base map;
d locate the points over which you will centre your circles/squares;
e draw the symbols and shade/colour;
f construct the scale used and title the completed map.

Your proportional symbols do not always have to be circles or squares. If the range between your maximum and minimum values is large, you might think of using a volumetric symbol. The only problem here is that you have to calculate the cube roots of the values!

## Review

4 Why might volumetric symbols be better than area symbols in coping with a large range in values?

5 Compare **Figures 4.6** and **4.7** in terms of their visual impact and ease of interpretation.

6 a On tracings of **Figure 4.1** plot the data in column B of **Figure 4.3** twice: (i) by proportional linear symbols and (ii) by proportional area symbols.

   b Which of the two maps do you think is the more satisfactory? Justify your view.

   c What do your completed maps tell you about the distribution of crime in Oxford?

# Pie charts

Pie charts are subdivided circles. They are frequently used on maps to show variations in the composition of a geographic phenomenon, for example agricultural land use on a farm-by-farm basis, or regional variations in the mix of employment (**Figure 4.8**). The pie chart may also be drawn proportional in size, to show an added dimension. In the case of the two examples, it would be variations in county size and in total population.

**Figure 4.8** Male employment in the UK

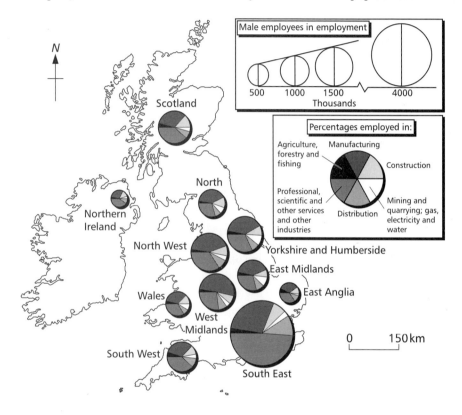

The following steps should be followed in the construction of a proportional pie chart map:

  **a** Convert your data into percentages. Each percent will be represented by a 3.6° slice of the circle.

  **b** Convert the percentages into degrees.

  **c** Follow steps (a), (b) and (c) in **section B** to determine the sizes of circles.

  **d** Draw circles appropriately located on your base map.

  **e** Subdivide the circles into sectors using the figures obtained in step (b).

  **f** Differentiate the sectors by means of either different shadings or colours.

  **g** Complete a key explaining the scheme of shadings and/or colours and giving the scale used in the construction of the circles.

  **h** Title the map.

Proportional pie charts can show a wide range of data and geographic variations. Care needs to be taken over their interpretation, remembering that circle size is showing absolute values and the sectors relative values.

It should also be pointed out that pie charts do not always have to be located on a map. They can be used quite effectively for showing the composition or make-up of things – for instance, the commodity structure of exports and imports, the energy sources used by a country, or the sectors of an economy. Where these sorts of data are available over a period of time, then a series of pie charts can be drawn to show change over time.

## Review

**7 a** From **Figure 4.3**, extract the crime data for the wards of Blackbird Leys, Central and Cherwell. Represent these data by means of proportional pie charts drawn on a tracing of **Figure 4.1**.

**b** Note any particular problems you may have encountered during the completion of the map.

**c** What observations would you make about crime in these different parts of Oxford?

**d** Suggest explanations for the points you have made in **c**.

## SECTION D

# Choropleths

A choropleth is a map which shows relative density per unit area (persons per km$^2$ or crop yield per hectare, for instance). Choropleth maps may also be used to represent percentages (e.g. per cent of households owning a car), ratios (e.g. cars per available parking space) and per capita information (e.g. average income), provided the values are related to a scheme of areas (such as wards, parishes, counties or countries). Choropleths are easy to construct and can give data a striking visual impact, as for example in showing the distribution of population in density terms (**Figure 4.9**). However, there are important limitations to bear in mind. Since each of the areas used in the compilation of the map shows only one value, there is the temptation to think that conditions are constant or uniform throughout an area. Where adjacent areas show different values, the boundary can appear to indicate a sharp contrast. Again, this may be somewhat removed from reality.

To draw a choropleth, five tasks must be carried out:

**Figure 4.9** The distribution of population in Japan

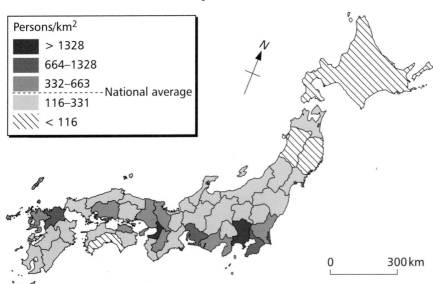

Persons/km$^2$
- > 1328
- 664–1328
- 332–663 — National average
- 116–331
- \\\ < 116

0    300 km

a collect and process the data to be mapped;
   b decide how many groups need to be defined to take in the maximum and minimum values;
   c define the statistical limits of those groups;
   d allocate each value to a group;
   e choose an appropriate shading for each group.

So far as the second task is concerned, it is customary to arrange the processed data in ascending or descending order. This allows us to see the range of values and also if there are any obvious groupings. Dividing the range between four and six groups is generally regarded as best. The fewer the number of groups, the greater the generalisation; the larger the number of groups, the greater the complexity and the challenge of interpretation. Groups must also be mutually exclusive – any one value may appear in one group only.

Groupings or classes can be defined using a number of different intervals:
   a arithmetic intervals, where the groups are of a uniform size, e.g. 0–4, 5–9, 10–14;
   b geometric intervals, where the groups increase in size by a regular ratio, e.g. 0–2, 3–6, 7–14, 15–30;
   c using standard deviations (see **Chapter 2**);
   d at natural breaks in the array of values (groups will therefore be of variable size);
   e by dividing the values in such a way that there is an equal number of values in each group.

**Figure 4.9** shows a slight variation, in that the geometric scale refers to the national average density figure. As a result, it is quite easy to identify those areas that are more and less densely populated than the national mean.

Shading should be done in one colour, although two colours can be used effectively, particularly where positive and negative values are being represented. Areas with the highest values should be shaded darkest and those with the lowest values lightest. This emphasises the importance of the greater density. If more than two colours are used it is important to use a conventional colour sequence, such as green > yellow > orange > brown, as used in the mapping of relief.

## Review

8 a Taking your data from **Figure 4.2** and on a tracing of **Figure 4.1** construct a choropleth map to show the distribution of unemployment in Oxford.
   b Justify the decisions you have taken with respect to the number and definition of groups.
   c Describe the pattern that you have shown.

9 a Using the values in column B of **Figure 4.3**, construct a choropleth map showing the distribution of crime in Oxford.

   b Compare your map with that of unemployment? What possible associations, if any, do you see?
(There are a number of key features to look out for when describing a map:
   ■ the highest value;
   ■ the lowest value;
   ■ the main trend or pattern;
   ■ any exceptions.
It is also important to name places and use the data. In this case you should refer to wards and give rates of reported crime.)

# Isolines

An isoline or isopleth is a line that joins points of equal value. There are many types of isopleth, for instance:

- contours – lines of equal height;
- isovels – lines of equal velocity;
- isobars – lines of equal pressure;
- isohyets – lines of equal precipitation;
- isotherms –lines of equal temperature.

Isolines allow us to see the distribution of a particular phenomenon, often over very large areas. Perhaps it is most useful in showing trends over space, and the gradients between high and low values. The weather map, with its pattern of isobars, is probably the best known example of an isoline map. The construction of an isoline map requires large amounts of data in the form of individual values for a network of specific points or places. The closer that network of points relative to area, the more accurate and detailed the isopleth map.

A critical step in the construction of an isopleth map is deciding the values to be represented by the isopleths. This requires sorting out what would be an appropriate value interval between consecutive isopleths. This, in turn, is strongly influenced by two considerations:

- the range of values to be plotted;
- the size of the area.

In general, we can say that the larger the range and the larger the area, the wider the value interval. It is the clarity of the message conveyed by the map that counts. Too close an interval over a large area can easily lead to a mass of confusing detail, whereas too wide an interval over a small area might render the map useless because of excessive generalisation.

In **Figure 4.10** an interval of 10 metres has been used. This seems about right for the scale of area involved. Once we have decided on an appropriate interval, we then have the sometimes tricky task of drawing the actual isopleths. It is important to draw the isopleths on the right side of the points and that we take trouble to plot the lines as accurately as possible between values.

## Review

**10** Make a tracing of the following diagram.

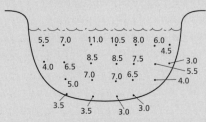

Stream velocities in a cross-section of a river

**a** Work out an appropriate isovel interval and draw the isovel pattern.

**b** Describe the essential features of the pattern.

**c** Give reasons for the pattern.

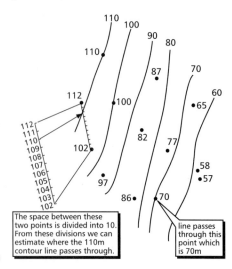

The space between these two points is divided into 10. From these divisions we can estimate where the 110m contour line passes through.

line passes through this point which is 70m

**Figure 4.10** Constructing contour lines

# Flow lines

Flow lines show the volume of movement between places. The thickness of the line indicates the volume, and the direction can be shown by an arrow. In many cases, absolute values are plotted, but in the case of **Figure 4.11**, data are in percentage form (per cent of total migrants to Mexico City). When using the technique it is important to:

- keep the background as simple as possible, so as to avoid clutter;
- choose an appropriate scale, so that extreme values can be shown without any loss of clarity;
- provide a key.

**11** Study **Figure 4.11**.

**a** What advantage, if any, is gained by using percentage rather than absolute figures?

**b** Write a brief account highlighting the main features of the migration pattern.

**Figure 4.11** The flow of migrants to Mexico City by birthplace

| | |
|---|---|
| 1 | Baja California (North) |
| 2 | Baja California (South) |
| 3 | Sonora |
| 4 | Chihuahua |
| 5 | Coahuila |
| 6 | Sinaloa |
| 7 | Durango |
| 8 | Nuevo Leon |
| 9 | Tamaulipas |
| 10 | San Luis Potosi |
| 11 | Zacatecas |
| 12 | Nayarit |
| 13 | Aguascalientes |
| 14 | Jalisco |
| 15 | Guanajuato |
| 16 | Queretaro |
| 17 | Hidalgo |
| 18 | Veracruz |
| 19 | Puebla |
| 20 | Tlaxcala |
| 21 | Mexico |
| 22 | Michoacan |
| 23 | Colima |
| 24 | Morelos |
| 25 | Guerrero |
| 26 | Oaxaca |
| 27 | Chiapas |
| 28 | Tabasco |
| 29 | Campeche |
| 30 | Quintana Roo |
| 31 | Yucatan |
| FD | Federal District |

# Sketch maps

A sketch is a rough drawing. It is not necessarily precise or accurate, but provides a general impression. A map, by contrast, is a flat representation of the ground. Hence, a sketch map is a rough outline or depiction of an area. It can vary in size, from a large-scale representation of a local area to a small-scale national map. In most individual projects, it is sketch maps of a local and regional scale that are most likely to be used. The key aspect of a sketch map is to get across important information. Sketch maps must never be included as inessential extras, but should be used as a simple way of getting over crucial information.

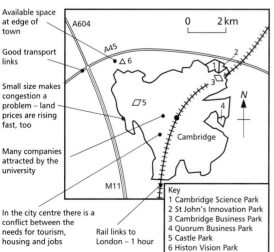

**Figure 4.12** Sketch map of science and business parks in Cambridge

Let us have a look at **Figure 4.12**. You will notice that it is very generalised; Cambridge is much more complex that the sketch suggests. However, the map does get important information across in a simple way. Hence, annotation and labelling are crucial. Notice how this simple sketch map:

- shows the important road links, especially the M11 and the A45;
- gives the distance and direction from London – this provides a regional setting;
- scatters 'key facts' around the map, to make it more interesting;
- stresses the links with the University and the quality of the work force;
- identifies some of the problems of the growth of Cambridge, such as congestion and high land prices.

**Figure 4.13** A sketch map of drainage and urban development in Oxford

Sketch maps which deal with physical geography should mention basic physical factors such as geology, slopes, altitude, permeability, soils and so on. These can be added in a box below the map if necessary, as shown in **Figure 4.13**. Alternatively, they can be shown on the sketch map itself.

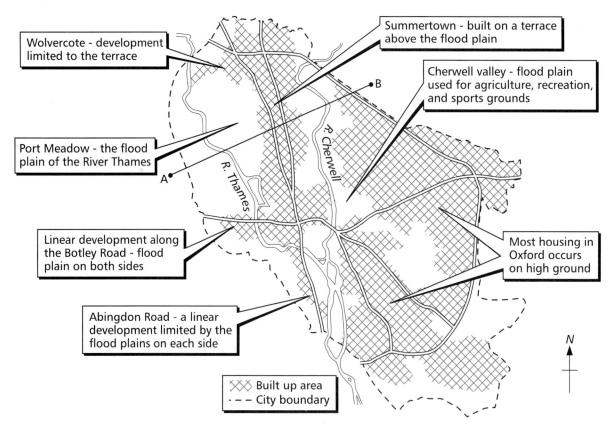

Annotating is certainly a useful technique, but it should not be restricted solely to maps and sketch maps. Sketch sections and other diagrams, together with photographs, can often benefit from annotations that seek to highlight the essential messages you wish to convey. **Figure 4.14** shows how an annotated sketch map may be derived from an aerial photograph.

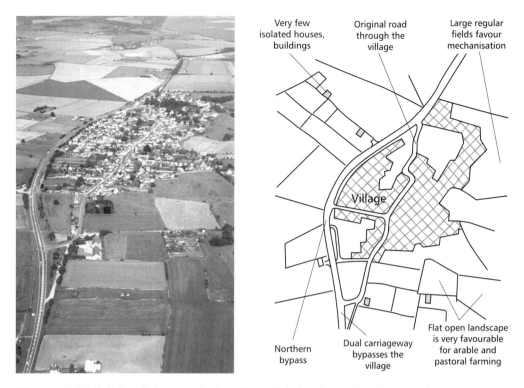

Figure 4.14 **(a)** Aerial photograph of a village, **(b)** sketch map based on the photo

Labels on sketch map:
- Very few isolated houses, buildings
- Original road through the village
- Large regular fields favour mechanisation
- Village
- Northern bypass
- Dual carriageway bypasses the village
- Flat open landscape is very favourable for arable and pastoral farming

## Review

12 Using the information in **Figure 4.13**, sketch the cross-section you would expect to find between points A and B. Annotate your sketch, paying particular attention to the relationship between urban development, geology, drainage and the risk of flooding.

**SECTION H**

# Summing up

In this chapter, we have considered just a small number of the cartographic techniques that you are likely to come across in your A-level course. However, those that have been selected for scrutiny are the ones most widely used in the compilation of reports based on the personal enquiry (see **Chapters 6** and **7**). What you will be expected to demonstrate then is not just an awareness of some of these techniques, but an ability to use the right one for the particular occasion.

## Review

13 Imagine you been asked to write a report on the distribution of total population and ethnic minorities in Oxford. There are relevant data in **Figure 4.2**. What maps might you produce to illustrate your report?

# 5

# Graphical techniques

Visual communication is an important aspect of Geography. Maps are perhaps the most distinctively geographical means of communication, but a whole range of other representational techniques can be used to report the results of geographical investigations. We have already looked at one device that does not need to be anchored to a map – the pie chart. But there are many others. These range from simple model diagrams and line graphs, to more complicated devices such as triangular graphs and compound bar charts. What follows is a highly selective sample, but it contains most of the techniques frequently used at A-level.

## SECTION A

## Systems diagrams

**Systems diagrams** mainly comprise annotations (often boxed), linked by lines and arrows. They are widely used in textbooks to put across basic concepts and ideas, as well as to portray the components and structures of systems (for example, the hydrological cycle, the ecosystem, etc.). In other words, they are simplifying devices which can be used to communicate quite complex relationships (**Figure 5.1**).

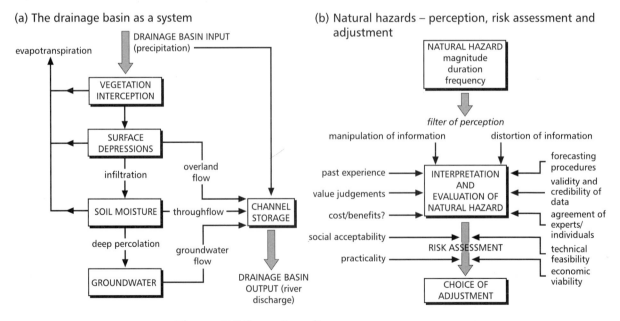

**Figure 5.1** Two systems diagrams

This sort of diagram is something you might also use in summarising your notes for revision purposes, or for working out how you are going to organise your personal enquiry. In the latter case, it can be a good way of ensuring that you work in a logical manner.

## Review

**1** Construct systems diagrams to represent the following:
- the slope as a system;
- the hydrological cycle;
- the relationships between climate, soils and vegetation in a tundra ecosystem;
- the downward spiral created by the closure of a factory;
- the possible links between unemployment, poor housing and crime;
- the economic ties between the Developing and Developed Worlds.

SECTION B

# Line graphs

Line graphs are quite simple graphs which are most frequently used to show changes over time – for instance, changes in temperature and precipitation over 12 months, or the growth in population over a period of years. Changes can be depicted in two ways, by either a continuous line or a series of proportional bars (**Figure 5.2**).

In all line graphs there are independent and dependent variables. For example, in **Figure 5.2** the temperature and rainfall figures are dependent variables, and the months of the year are the independent variable – the former are, in a sense, 'dependent' on the latter. The convention of graph construction requires that the independent variable is plotted on the horizontal or x axis, and the dependent is plotted on the vertical or y axis. For each pair of data (e.g. mean temperature for January), project a line from the corresponding x and y axes. Mark with a dot the point where the two lines meet. When all the data have been plotted, join up successive points either by means of a straight line or a curving one that ultimately rounds the ups and downs.

It is important to label the axis and to show the scale clearly. Another important aspect of graph construction is the choosing a scale for the x axis that is appropriate for the range in values to be plotted.

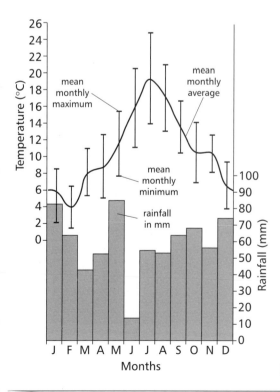

**Figure 5.2** Climate graph for Oxford

Multiple or compound line graphs can show changes in more than one variable, as for example in precipitation and stream discharge (the hydrograph). Such diagrams can reveal significant relationships between the variables. It might be the changing balance of exports and imports, shifts in the relative importance of energy sources, or just changing shopping habits. On such graphs, data may be plotted in a number of different forms – in absolute terms, cumulatively, or in percentage form (**Figure 5.3 (a), (b) and (c)** respectively). (Note that **Figure 5.3 (a)** uses a semi-logarithmic graph, because inflation since 1945 has caused the value range to become very stretched.)

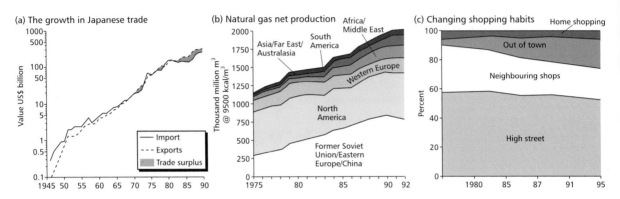

**Figure 5.3** Three different types of compound graph

Finally, it needs to be remembered that time does not necessarily have to be one of the variables of a line graph. The techniques may also be used to the show relationships between other variables, as for example the changes in water velocity or quality along a river's course. The hydrograph, which shows the relationship between precipitation and run-off, is probably one of best-known examples of such a line graph.

## Review

2 Draw a line graph to represent the following data. The distance between each sampling site is 50 metres.

| Site | Temperature (°C) | Oxygen content (mg $O_2$/l) |
|------|------------------|------------------------------|
| 1 | 18.0 | 0.12 |
| 2 | 17.8 | 0.14 |
| 3 | 17.8 | 0.12 |
| 4 | 21.3 | 0.11 |
| 5 | 21.6 | 1.84 |
| 6 | 22.4 | 1.71 |
| 7 | 21.4 | 1.33 |
| 8 | 22.0 | 1.54 |
| 9 | 21.7 | 1.45 |
| 10 | 21.5 | 1.60 |

a Which is the independent variable?
b How have you solved the problem of having to produce two scales?
c How did you arrive at suitable scales?
d What are the main hydrological messages conveyed by the graph?

# Logarithmic graphs

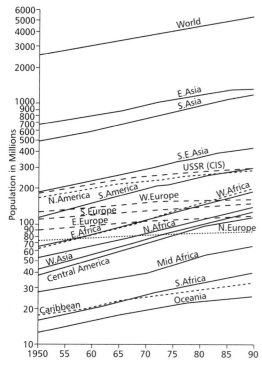

**Figure 5.4** World population growth, 1950–90

Semi-logarithmic graph paper has a 'normal' scale on one axis – usually the horizontal or y axis – and a logarithmic scale on the other. Semi-log graphs are used to show data that have a particularly wide range of values. For example, a semi-log graph allows us to compare things that differ enormously in size. **Figure 5.4** allows us to compare Oceania and East Asia in terms of their trends in absolute population growth; world population growth is also thrown in for good measure! This would not really be feasible using ordinary graph paper.

The logarithmic scale compresses the range of values. It gives more space to the smaller values and reduces the amount of space for the larger values. Thus it can shows relative growth quite clearly. On the scale there are 'cycles' of values. Each cycle increases by a larger amount, usually to the power of 10. Thus on **Figure 5.4**, the first cycle increases by 10 each time to 100, the second cycle increases by 100 to 1 000, and so.

In some cases, logarithmic scales can be used on both axes. This would be recommended where the two sets of data to be plotted both have large ranges. Although not a line graph as such, you see that logarithmic scales have been used in **Figure 5.7**.

## Review

**3** Set down the advantages and disadvantages of using logarithmic graph scales.

# Scatter graphs

Scatter graphs show how two sets of data are related to each other, for example, population size and number of services, or distance from the source of a river and average pebble size. They are often used alongside Spearman's rank correlation coefficient which tests if there is a statistical relationship between two sets of data. To plot a scatter graph, decide which variable is independent. In **Figure 5.5** organic content is the independent variable, moisture content the dependent. The method of data plotting is exactly the same as for the line graph.

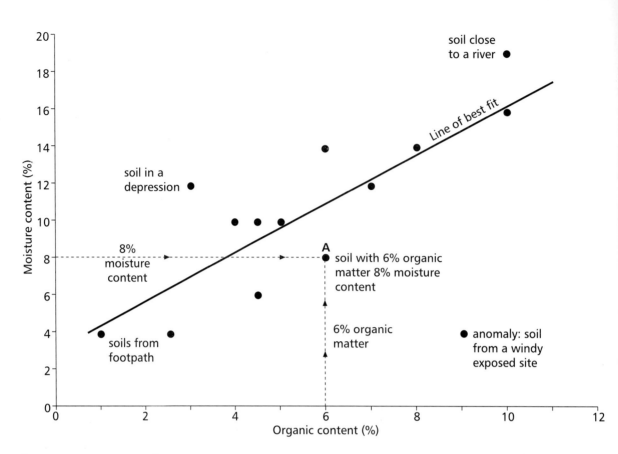

**Figure 5.5** A scatter graph of the relationship between soil organic content and moisture

When all the data have been plotted, it is customary to identify the general trend. The trend is indicated by a straight line, which is known as the **best-fit line**. It should be drawn through the points in such a way as to keep the distances from the line to the points equal above and below the line. Points well away from the line are known as residuals and should be ignored.

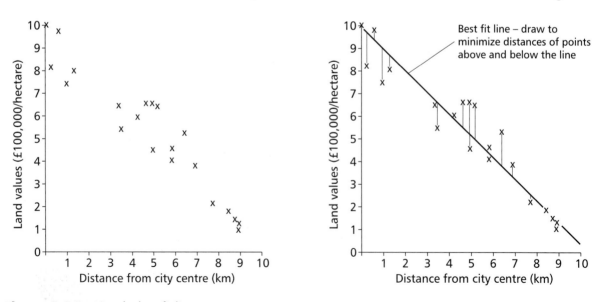

**Figure 5.6** Drawing the best-fit line

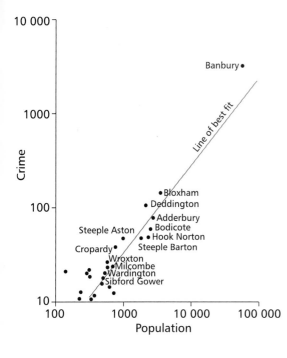

The type of correlation revealed by the best-fit line is known as **graphical correlation**. In this case, the relationship between land values and distance from the city centre is negative – that is, as distance from the city centre increases, land values decrease. A best-fit line trending from the bottom left of the scatter graph to the top right would indicate a positive graphical correlation (**Figure 5.7**).

In **Figure 5.7** the intention is to establish whether the frequency of crime simply increases in direct proportion to the increase in settlement size. Because both sets of data have large ranges, logarithmic scales have been used on both axes of the graph.

**Figure 5.7** Scatter graph of settlement size and recorded crime

## Review

4 a Construct a scatter graph using the following data:

| Site | Discharge (m³/sec) | Suspended load (g/m³) |
|------|--------------------|-----------------------|
| 1 | 0.45 | 10.8 |
| 2 | 0.42 | 9.7 |
| 3 | 0.51 | 11.2 |
| 4 | 0.55 | 11.3 |
| 5 | 0.68 | 12.5 |
| 6 | 0.75 | 12.8 |
| 7 | 0.89 | 13.0 |
| 8 | 0.76 | 12.7 |
| 9 | 0.96 | 13.0 |
| 10 | 1.26 | 17.4 |

b Draw in the best-fit line.
c What is the nature of the graphical correlation?
d Are there any residuals? If so, circle the points on the scatter graph.

5 Write a brief account based on your interpretation of **Figure 5.7**.

# Polar graphs

A polar graph or rose diagram is used to show direction as well as magnitude. For example, **Figure 5.8(a)** shows the direction that cirques in the Lake District face. It is quite clear from the diagram that most face northwards and eastwards, whereas there are relatively few that face south and west. Similarly, **Figure 5.8(b)** shows the orientation of the long axes of pebbles in glacial deposits. Here it can be seen that glacier movement has been predominantly south-westwards, but there is some evidence for a lesser south-eastwards movement.

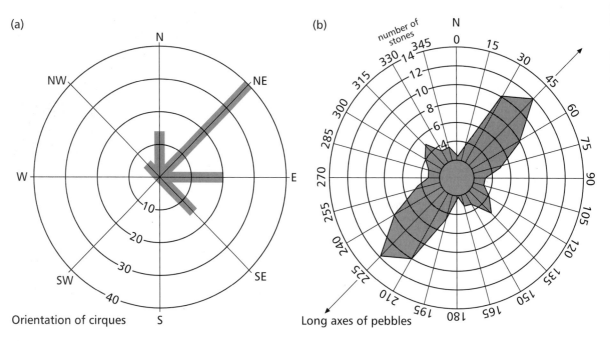

(a) Orientation of cirques

(b) Long axes of pebbles

**Figure 5.8** Polar graphs and the study of glaciation

The method for constructing a polar graph is quite simple. Using a compass and a protractor, lines are drawn that correspond to north (0°), north-east (45°), east (90°), south-east (135°), south (180°), south-west (225°), west (270°), and north-west (315°). A scale is used; in this case it relates to the radius of the diagram. As with all graphs, particular attention should be paid to the selection of an appropriate scale for the range of values. It is best to plot the chosen scale on the vertical (north) axis. Using a compass, project the lines around the graph. Then plot the data for each directional sector.

It is possible to make these diagrams more detailed. For example, rather than just having a solid bar to show the total value recorded in a particular direction, the bar could be divided. In the case of a wind rose it might show the percentage frequency of different wind speeds. This is especially important in coastal studies, as it is not just the frequency of wind direction, but the magnitude which is important.

**6** The second column in the table below shows the frequency of wind direction on a stretch of the Dorset coast.

    **a** Draw a polar graph of wind direction.
    **b** Now divide each wind direction to show wind speed frequencies.

| | Freq | Percentage frequency of wind speeds (knots) | | | | | | |
|---|---|---|---|---|---|---|---|---|
| | (%) | 0–4.9 | 5–9.9 | 10–14.9 | 15–19.9 | 20–24.9 | 25–29.9 | ≥ 30 |
| N | 12 | 0 | 2 | 1 | 4 | 1 | 2 | 2 |
| NE | 9 | 0 | 0 | 3 | 5 | 1 | 0 | 0 |
| E | 7 | 1 | 0 | 2 | 1 | 2 | 0 | 1 |
| SE | 14 | 2 | 1 | 4 | 3 | 2 | 1 | 1 |
| S | 21 | 2 | 5 | 9 | 4 | 1 | 0 | 0 |
| SW | 14 | 1 | 2 | 4 | 4 | 3 | 0 | 0 |
| W | 13 | 0 | 2 | 3 | 4 | 3 | 1 | 0 |
| NW | 10 | 0 | 1 | 2 | 3 | 1 | 2 | 1 |

    **c** What does your diagram show?
    **d** Why do think such a polar graph would be useful in a coastal study

**SECTION F**

# Triangular graphs

Triangular graphs are used to represent data that can be divided into three parts, e.g. soil (sand, silt and clay), employment (primary, secondary and tertiary), and population (young, adult and elderly). It requires that data are in percentage form and totals. The main advantage of the triangular graph is that it allows a large amount of data to be shown on one diagram – think how many pie charts or bar charts would be used to show all the data shown on **Figure 5.9**. In many cases, once plotted, value groupings  become evident – in the case of soils, groups of soil texture. Triangular graphs can be tricky to construct – it is easy to get confused. However, with care they can provide a fast and reliable way of classifying large amounts of data which have three components.

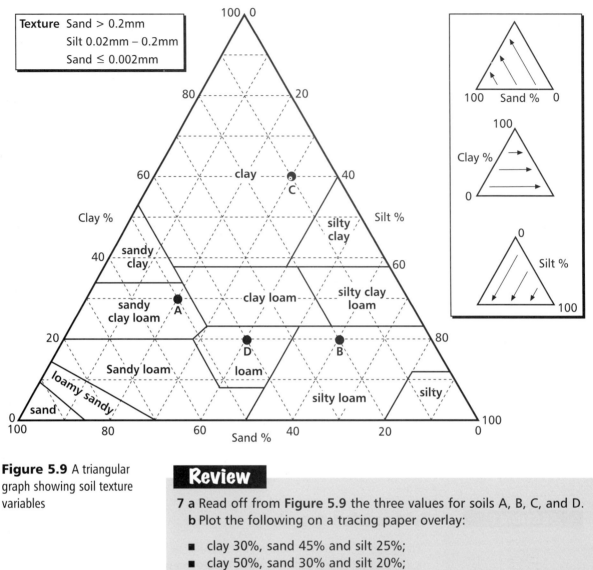

**Figure 5.9** A triangular graph showing soil texture variables

**Review**

**7 a** Read off from **Figure 5.9** the three values for soils A, B, C, and D.
**b** Plot the following on a tracing paper overlay:

- clay 30%, sand 45% and silt 25%;
- clay 50%, sand 30% and silt 20%;
- clay 20%, sand 35% and silt 45%;
- clay 37%, sand 36% and silt 27%.

**SECTION G**

## Bar charts

Bar charts are one of the simplest ways of presenting data. Each bar in such a chart is of a standard width, but the length or height is directly proportional to the value being represented. Bar charts can assume a variety of different forms. There are three basic types.

**Simple** bar charts show a single factor. They are probably best used when you want to compare point values on a map (**Figure 4.6**). Multiple bar charts or **histograms** are used to group together data for a particular place, or more often to show changing frequencies in a variable over time. We are already aware that they are used to show monthly precipitation totals (**Figure 5.2**).

**Compound** bar charts basically involve subdivision of a simple bar or bars. For example, the bar might be proportional to total imports, and be subdivided on the basis of its commodity composition. A combination of compound and multiple bar charts would serve well in terms of showing how quantity and composition change over time. **Figure 5.10** shows the changing relative importance of various imported commodities, but neglects to show how the overall volume of imports has changed over the period.

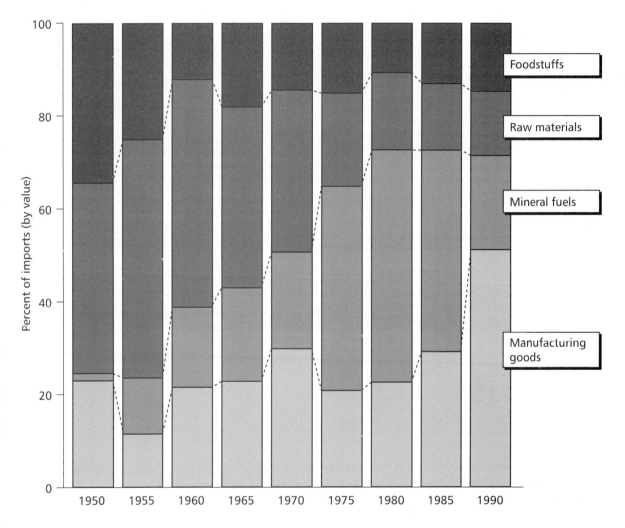

**Figure 5.10** The changing composition of Japanese imports

The scale of a bar chart can be adapted to show positive and negative features. This is sometimes referred to as a divergent graph (**Figure 5.11**). In some cases, if the range of values is very large it is best to split the scale by means of broken lines.

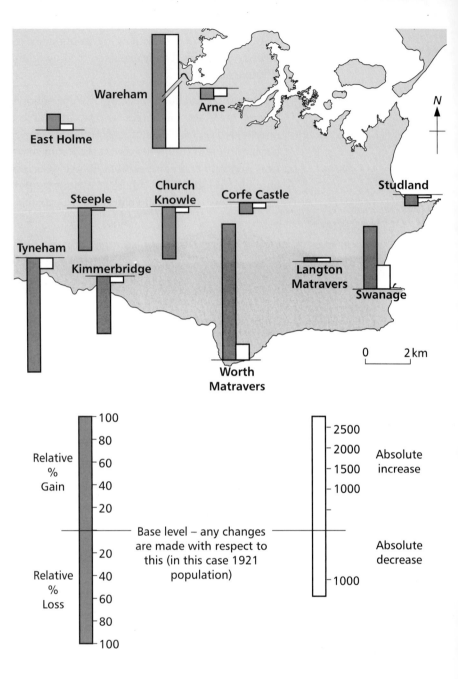

**Figure 5.11** Absolute and percentage population change in the Isle of Purbeck

One widely used variant of the histogram is the age–sex pyramid. This is constructed in 1-, 5- or 10-year age groups, with males on one side and females on the other. This almost invariably takes the form of a pyramid, with the youngest age group at the base and the oldest at the top (**Figure 5.12**). The horizontal bars are drawn proportional in length to either the percentage of the total population or the actual number in each age group. Complete pyramids analysing a population at different times can reveal some interesting shifts in structure, particularly so far as age is concerned.

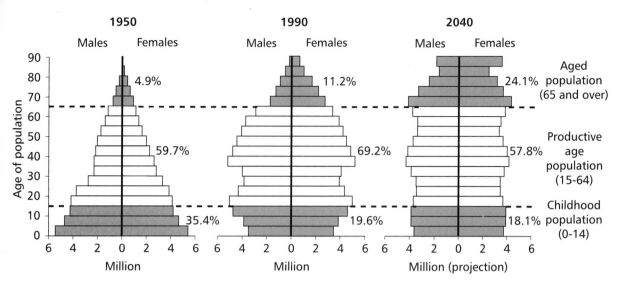

| | 1950 | 1990 | 2040 | |
|---|---|---|---|---|

**Figure 5.12** Changes in the Japanese age–sex pyramid

**SECTION H**

# Dispersion diagrams

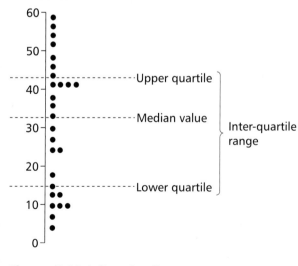

**Figure 5.13** A dispersion diagram

A dispersion diagram is a very useful diagram for showing the range of a set of data, their tendency to group or disperse, and also for comparing two sets of data. It involves plotting the values of a single variable on a vertical axis. Technically, there is a short horizontal axis showing frequency (**Figure 5.13**). What it is revealed is the frequency distribution. Dispersion diagrams can also be used to determine the class intervals for choropleths maps (**Chapter 4 section D**).

A critical part of analysing any array of values by means of the dispersion diagram is to determine the median, upper and lower quartile values and therefore the inter-quartile range (see **Chapter 2 section C**) (**Figure 5.13**).

**Figure 5.14** The incidence of lichen on east- and west-facing gravestones

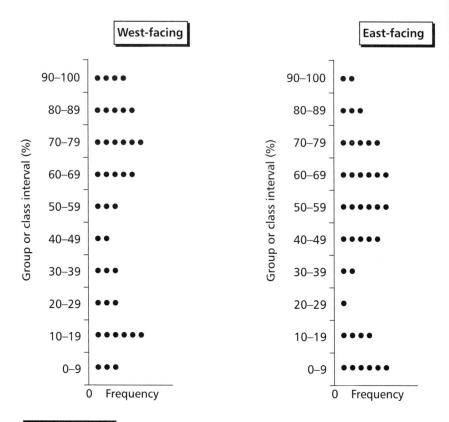

## Review

10 **Figure 5.14** shows the incidence of lichens on east- and west-facing gravestones in Cassington, Oxon.
   **a** Plot the medians and quartiles and compare the two frequency distributions.
   **b** Give reasons for your results.

11 The following data relate to the size of pebbles (mm) in two samples, one taken from the upper course of a Lake District stream and the other from its lower course.

Upper Course: 32, 45, 21, 34, 48, 23, 24, 37, 43, 27, 56, 46, 37, 32, 45, 51, 20, 43, 38, 36, 26, 45, 19, 40, 46, 32, 56, 39, 30, 43.

Lower Course: 23, 12, 17, 26, 10, 9, 25, 31, 25, 30, 16, 19, 12, 19, 22, 13, 25, 9, 12, 31, 26, 18, 23, 31, 20, 12, 16, 27, 18, 23.

   **a** Draw two dispersion diagrams, using the same scale on each.
   **b** To what extent are the two samples different?
   **c** How might you explain what you have found?

# Cumulative frequency diagrams

The cumulative frequency diagram or polygon is another technique for analysing frequency distributions. Rather than plotting a single discrete frequency for each value, the frequency figures are simply added successively as one moves up the scale from low to high values.

**Figure 5.15** A cumulative frequency polygon and box-and-whisker diagram

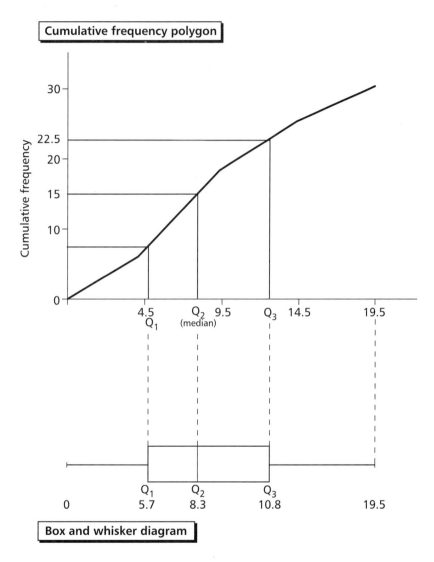

Figure 5.15 shows data relating to the frequency of slopes of different angles. In all, 30 slopes were surveyed, so the y axis is drawn to accommodate a maximum value of 30. Four different groups of slope angle were recognised: 0–4.5° (6), 4.6–9.5° (12), 9.6–14.5° (7) and 14.6–19.5°(5). The upper value of each group is shown on the x axis. The number in brackets refers to the number of slopes recorded in the group. Four points are plotted on the graph: 6 x 4.5°, 18 (6 + 12) x 9.5°, 25 (6 + 12 + 7) x 14.5° and 30 (6 + 12 + 7 + 5) x 19.5°. In other words, the frequencies have been added (so they are cumulative) and plotted against the upper value of each slope group.

A particular feature of such a graph is that the median and quartile values can easily be identified by dividing the x axis into four equal parts and then at each of the three boundaries reading off the value on the y axis. A box-and-whiskers diagram can be plotted by projecting down the three quartile values. This gives a simplified representation of the total and inter-quartile ranges.

## Review

**12** Extract the data shown in **Figure 2.8** and represent in the form of a cumulative frequency polygon and box-whisker diagram.

**SECTION J**

# Bipolar analysis

Bipolar analysis is a technique for comparing things – areas, people or simply two or three sets of results. The example below shows how it can be used in the visual portrayal of the results of a questionnaire.

In a questionnaire survey, 50 shoppers were asked to rate two different shopping centres according to a range of criteria and on a scale of 1 to 5, with 5 being the highest score. (There is nothing significant about this scale; it could easily have been 1 to 10. It was felt in this particular instance that a scale any greater than 1 to 5 would have been too off-putting to the interviewees.) Once the results have been collated, the average value for each criterion is calculated. This number can be rounded either up or down to the nearest whole number. A dot is then placed in the

**Figure 5.16** Bipolar analysis of shopping centre survey

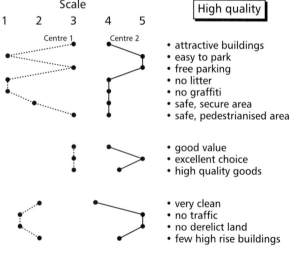

relevant box on the diagram (**Figure 5.16**). Once this has been done for every category, all the dots are joined up with a line. It is then very easy to make a visual comparison of the centres by simply looking at their respective lines.

**Figure 5.16** clearly shows that the new shopping centre (2) is perceived to be more attractive than the established centre (1). The aspects of the former that are emphasised are its provision of plenty of parking spaces, its cleanliness, safety, pedestrianisation and its variety of shops. In contrast, centre 2 is downgraded for such things as graffiti and litter, poor parking, its high crime rate and concern about personal safety.

## Review

13 The following results were found from an environmental and amenity survey of three wards in Oxford: Blackbird Leys (B), East (E) and Wolvercote (W). The scores are on a scale of 1 to 5 (poor to good)

| Environmental quality | E | B | W | |
|---|---|---|---|---|
| very dirty | 4 | 2 | 5 | very clean |
| heavy traffic | 3 | 1 | 5 | no traffic |
| much derelict land | 4 | 4 | 5 | no derelict land |
| many high-rise buildings | 2 | 2 | 4 | few high-rise buildings |

| Amenities | | | | |
|---|---|---|---|---|
| no open or green space | 5 | 5 | 3 | much open or green space |
| no shops | 2 | 4 | 2 | wide range of shops |
| no recreational facilities | 4 | 2 | 2 | many facilities |
| no schools | 4 | 3 | 1 | primary and secondary |
| no social services | 4 | 3 | 2 | satisfactory provision |

a Plot the bipolar graph for these three areas.
b How do they compare in terms of environmental quality and amenity provision?
c Are you able to offer any explanation for the differences? You might refer to **Figures 4.1, 4.2** and **4.3**

# Summing up

That completes our look at a range of graphical techniques that you might consider using when you come to prepare the report of your personal enquiry (**Chapters 6** and **7**). You may have noticed that virtually all of them make use of the graph principle, and most are to do with the representation of frequency values of some sort or another. Perhaps the most crucial point of all, though, is knowing the strengths and weaknesses of each technique, and when it is most appropriate to use them.

## Review

**14** What graphical techniques might you use in the following investigations to **(a)** analyse data and **(b)** present your results:
- finding out the degree of accordance in summit heights in an upland area;
- establishing rainfall reliability at a weather station;
- seeing how soil depth varies with slope angle;
- assessing the quality of housing in different areas;
- showing how land use in your home parish has changed over the last 50 years;
- comparing the economic sectors of three countries;
- investigating settlement size frequency in a county;
- a questionnaire survey of village commuters about their mode of travel?

Justify your choices by reference to other possible techniques.

# CHAPTER 6

# Investigative techniques for the personal enquiry

This chapter covers some techniques which might be useful in collecting data for your personal enquiry. Relevant techniques of analysis and presentation are dealt with elsewhere in this book.

**SECTION A**

## Sampling

A sample is a representative body of data. A large number of items (the population) can be represented by a small subsection (the sample). Sampling is an efficient way of using time, energy and resources which allows us to make reliable statements about the whole population. Sampling is used in personal enquiries because it would most often be either impractical or impossible in terms of time, money and labour to study the entire area or the whole population. A resort to sampling makes things manageable; it is the sensible way forward. Various sampling methods are available to give an accurate 'taste' of an area and its data.

In general, there are two broad types of sampling: **spatial** sampling and **temporal** sampling. Spatial sampling involves taking samples of one or more variables regardless of time changes, whilst temporal sampling involves recording change in one or more variables over a period of time. Both types of sampling can be broken down into three further sub-categories: **systematic** sampling, **random** sampling and **stratified** sampling (**Figure 6.1**).

**Figure 6.1** Types of spatial sampling

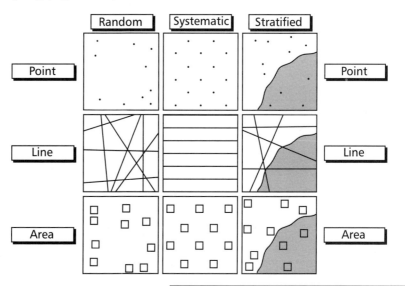

There are a number of key questions to ask before the sample is taken.

- What is the population being studied, and over what area and/or time?
- What method of sampling would be most appropriate for the enquiry topic?
- What is the minimum size of sample needed in order to produce reliable information and results?

## Random sampling

In random samples, each item has an equal chance of being picked. Randomness is best achieved by resort to a random numbers table (see **Appendix Table 3**). This is a table with no bias in the sequence of numbers. Once a number is chosen it can be related to a grid reference, an angular direction and/or a distance (**Figure 6.1**). This allows an unbiased sample to be taken from the area in question. Even so, as with all types of sampling, there are still some problems. For example, the random sample may miss an entire part of the survey area, as a result of the numbers that the table produces.

## Systematic sampling

Using random numbers to generate truly random samples is time-consuming; systematic sampling is much easier and quicker. In a systematic sample, items are chosen at regular intervals – for example every 5 metres, or every tenth person, and so on. But here again it is possible that the sampling procedure may miss out important geographic features. This might be illustrated by assuming that **Figure 6.1** shows a systematic sample across a ploughed field. In a study of soil temperature and soil moisture, such a systematic sample might pick out only the crests or only the troughs in the field. This would give an unreliable representation of the true soil conditions. The major problem with this type of sampling is that it can easily give a biased result because the sample is too small and as a consequence large areas are not included in the sample.

## Stratified sampling

If it is known that there are important groups or classes in a population, such as different rock types in an area, or different racial groups in a city, it is possible to make sure that a representative sample of them is included in a survey. This is known as stratified sampling. For example, an area can be divided up into areas of differing geology as shown by the shading on **Figure 6.1**. In each of these areas a sample would then be taken. This could be a random sample or a systematic sample. Likewise in a survey of people, if we knew that 35 per cent of the population were elderly, 50 per cent were adult of working age and 15 per cent were under the age of 15 years, we might wish to interview people in those proportions to achieve a fair range of replies. If the sample size were 100, we would continue to interview adults of working age until we had 50 replies, elderly people until we had 35 replies and young people until we had 15 replies. If we found that we had 15 replies from young people in the first 50 samples we could then ignore young people from our questionnaire and concentrate on gathering the rest of the sample of elderly people and adults of working age.

## Sample size

Determining the appropriate size of a sample is a critical matter. In some respects it very much depends on the nature and aims of the investigation. There are formulae for helping decide what would be right by way of sample size for a particular survey. Much rests on the **confidence limits** that you want to place on the results you derive from your sample (**Chapter 3 section C**). However, the easiest way to decide on both the sample size and what it means for the confidence limits is to use **Appendix Table 4**. Referring to this table, if for example a sample of 100 people were interviewed in a questionnaire survey and 90 per cent of them said that they preferred to shop at a particular centre, the real figure (at the 95 per cent confidence level) actually lies between 96 per cent (i.e. 90% + 6%) and 84 per cent (90% – 6%). The decision on sample size should be made by reading across the 50 per cent row in **Table 4**. This represents the worst-case scenario. If you would be satisfied with a maximum margin of error of plus or minus 10 per cent, a survey sample of 100 would be acceptable. If not, then note that doubling the sample size would only reduce the margin to plus or minus 7.1 per cent.

Again, it needs to be stressed that the data being sampled have a normal distribution (**Figure 2.6**). In such a distribution 50 per cent of the values are above the mean, 50 per cent of the values are below the mean and most of the values are within 1 standard deviation of the mean. Probability holds that in a normal distribution:

- 68 per cent of samples lie within ± 1 standard deviation of the mean;
- 95 per cent of samples lie within ±2 standard deviations of the mean; and
- 99.9 per cent of samples lie within ± 3 standard deviations of the mean.

In other words, there is less than a 1 in 100 chance that the mean lies outside the sample mean ± 3 standard deviations, and a less than 1 in 20 chance that the sample mean lies outside the sample mean ± 2 standard deviations (**Chapter 3 section B**).

## Review

1 a Assess the relative merits of the three types of sampling.

  b Cite one example when each would be the preferred sampling strategy.

# Surveys in physical geography

Sampling is a crucial aspect of much of the survey work undertaken in physical geography. It is probably true to say that the majority of personal enquiry topics today fall within physical rather than human geography. There is a whole host of aspects that might be investigated. What follows are some of the most popular areas of survey and research.

## Slopes

Slopes are the basic building-blocks of landforms. There are a number of ways of measuring them, involving different types of survey equipment.

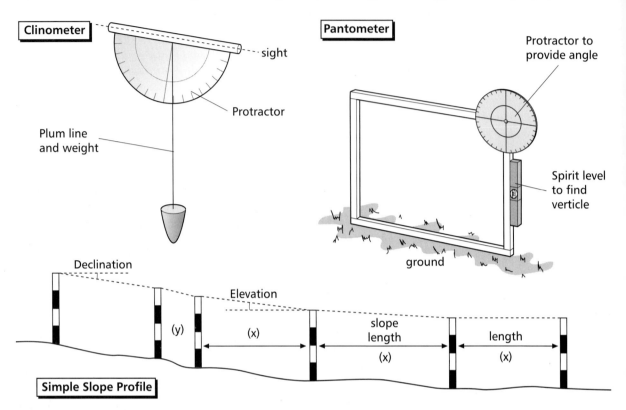

**Figure 6.2** Different ways of measuring slopes

- Using a **clinometer**. This is a protractor with a weight on it; it is aligned with the slope and the angle is read off. Needless to say, it is not terribly accurate.
- Using a **pantometer**. This is a collapsible parallelogram which can be place against a slope. Slope angles are then read from a protractor placed on the vertical.
- An **Abney level** measures the angle of inclination or declination between the line of sight and the horizontal. Both measurements are taken at any one time and compared. In theory, they should be the same, but operator error may produce different readings. An average of the two is taken for each slope unit.
- **Levelling** measures height differences over a given length of slope. A simple method is to use three 1-metre or 2-metre rules and to measure the height variations over each metre or 2 metres. This generates a large amount of data and is excellent for surveying small-scale landforms, but for larger landforms it is too time-consuming.

Slope angles are usually measured over a fixed length, normally 5 or 10 metres. If there many small-scale variations, a shorter length may be more appropriate. On more uniform slopes, it would be permissible to measure over a longer slope length.

## Streams

Stream studies are of paramount popularity – something which is not readily comprehensible! Maybe it's the appeal of playing with water! There are a number of stream characteristics that lend themselves to survey and investigation:

- downstream changes in channel width and depth;
- patterns of stream velocity;
- the quantity and character of bedload;
- water quality.

Such aspects of streams readily lend themselves to statements in the form of hypotheses.

Measuring the width and depth of a stream is quite straightforward. Place ranging-rods at either edge of the channel and measure the width across. Then measure the depth of the stream at regular intervals, say every 50 cm. Remember it is important to estimate 'bankfull volume', so as well as measuring the profile of the river as it is at the time of survey, also measure from the top of the channel.

**Figure 6.3** Stream survey work under way. Streams in winter can be cold and deep. Make sure help is at hand.

There are two ways of measuring stream velocity. The ideal piece of equipment is the **flow meter**, which gives readings in terms of metres or centimetres per second. The pattern of velocity across a stream can be measured at regular intervals and at regular depths (both intervals being determined by the overall dimensions of the stream). Comparing the pattern of isovels in a meander with that on a straight section of channel can make for an interesting investigation.

In the absence of a flow meter, an orange can be substituted, This should be thrown into a stream at a fixed point, and the time it takes to travel 10 metres recorded. Take at least six readings at each place in order to achieve a reliable estimate of the velocity. Because velocity at the surface of the stream is greater than the average velocity of the whole stream, multiply your mean measurement by 0.8 to give a more realistic reading. (Just one word of warning: unless you are able to recover the orange, this could end up being quite an expensive survey!)

Measurements of bedload are quite easy to make and are capable of yielding considerable amounts of information. Take a random sample of 30 pieces of bedload from selected points along the course of the stream. The expectation is that river sediments become smaller and rounder downstream as a result of longer attrition. Thus we can compare the mean length (long axis) and shape (degree of roundness) of each sample of 30 stones, to determine whether our observations are in line with the expected.

Finally, there are aspects of water quality that can be fairly easily monitored at regularly spaced sample points along a stream. These include:

- temperature – using an electronic thermometer;
- pH level – using a pH probe;
- detergent content – half fill a clear sample bottle, shake it vigorously and time how long it takes for the froth to clear;
- ion concentrations (ammonia, chlorides, nitrates and phosphates) – using HACH test kits;
- evidence of pollution – dead fish, oil, smell, discoloration, etc.

## Coasts

Much of the survey work in coastal studies focuses on the profiles and materials of beaches. Here the same techniques apply as already outlined: slope measuring techniques for the profiles, and bedload analysis for beach material. The former are also relevant to another popular topic, namely studies of sand dunes which are mostly based on cross-sections and which involve testing any one of a number of hypotheses (**Figure 6.4**).

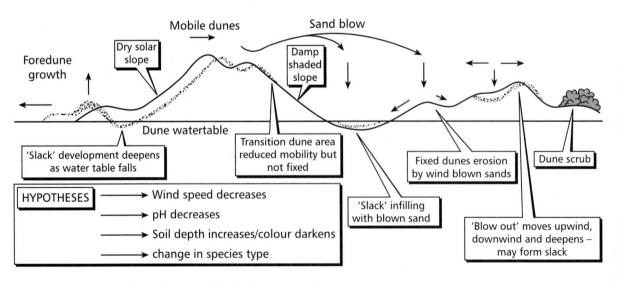

**Figure 6.4** The dynamic dune environment

## Soils

There are many simple but excellent surveys that can be carried out on soils. For example, surveys might investigate:

- the effect of slope angle on soils thickness;
- the variation in soils with geology;
- the relationship between moisture and organic content.

Let us take up the last of these. Take a sample of soil with an auger or small trowel. Place a handful of the soil in an airtight bag. To measure moisture content, weigh a sample of the soil ($S_1$). Place it in an oven and heat it at 100°C for 24 hours. Review the sample ($S_2$). The moisture content is found by the formula:

$$\frac{S_1 - S_2}{S_2} \times 100.$$

To work out the organic content, take the sample $S_2$ and burn it over a bunsen burner at maximum heat for 15 minutes. Reweigh the burned sample ($S_3$). The organic content is found by the formula:

$$\frac{S_2 - S_3}{S_3} \times 100.$$

This sort of investigation can be taken further. For example, before 'processing' the soil sample, why not take a pH reading? After burning off the organic matter ($S_3$), sieve the soil sample and work out the proportions of the soil that are sand, silt and clay. These are the main components of soil texture.

**Figure 6.5** It is always useful to have more than one person carrying out an enquiry – not just for safety, but for measuring and recording results.

We can also investigate **soil depth** (from the surface to the bedrock) and **soil horizons**. The former needs an auger and an agreed network or transect of sampling points. Ideally, the latter needs exposure of the horizon by digging. (Before you attempt this, it is vital that you obtain permission to do so from the landowner, and that once you have completed your sketching and analysis, you replace all the excavated material.)

## Vegetation

Much work on vegetation involves sampling and the use of a **quadrat**. At each sampling point, the quadrat (usually a metre square) is placed on the ground and a number of different aspects of the vegetation may be enumerated. These would include **diversity** (the number of different species present), **density** (the degree to which the ground is covered) and **development** (height). Using the quadrat method it is possible to investigate spatial changes in vegetation, such as with altitude and with distance from the coast.

**SECTION C**

# Questionnaires

A questionnaire is a set of prearranged questions which seeks information from people. The questions in geographical investigations normally cover features such as:

- background characteristics – the age, sex and occupation – of the sample population;
- patterns of behaviour – such as shopping, work, transport and recreation;
- views and attitudes concerning contemporary issues.

There are a number of points to consider when planning a questionnaire.

- What questions to ask?
- How long should the questionnaire be?
- How will the questions strengthen the broader enquiry?
- How many people should be questioned?
- What type of people should be questioned?
- Where will completion of the questionnaire take place?

Questions are often divided into three main types: open, closed and scale questions.

**Open questions** allow the interviewee to respond freely and at length. However, it is often difficult to analyse such data. Open-ended questions, such as 'What is your opinion on the proposed by-pass?' do not guide or discipline respondents in their answers. Such questions are useful because of their flexibility, allowing greater detail and individuality. However, they are often difficult to code and/or quantify. Recording replies to these questions can be a problem.

By contrast, **closed questions** allow the interviewee only a fixed number of responses, such as yes/no, multiple choice, and 'on a scale of 1 to 10...'. Fixed-response questions are the most frequently used in questionnaires. For example, a fixed-response question would be: 'How did you travel to the city centre – by bus, car, train, bicycle, walk or other?' Such questions have a number of advantages and disadvantages. Advantages include greater uniformity of measurement, greater reliability and easier coding. On the other hand, they may suffer from superficiality and can sometimes provoke irritability in the respondent, who finds none of the alternatives really appropriate to his or her circumstances and is thereby perhaps forced into an inappropriate response.

**Scale questions**, are those that take the form: 'Arrange the following factors in order of importance', or 'How do you rate the quality of service on a scale of 1 to 5?' Since they encourage a degree of uniformity in their responses, they are relatively easy to code and analyse. However, if they are too simple the information that they yield can be of very limited value.

Questionnaires should be concise and to the point. Most respondents are busy people with their minds set on things other than answering questions posed by strangers. Hence the questionnaire should ideally not cover more than a side of A4 paper (and certainly not more than one sheet). The number of questions should be severely restricted. Equally, there should not be too few. Having been stopped in the street, respondents may feel somewhat cheated if they are only asked a couple of general questions. Somewhere between six and 12 questions usually 'feels' about right.

Questionnaires should follow a logical sequence. At the start, you should introduce yourself and explain the nature and purpose of the enquiry. Simple background questions should appear first, with the more specific, complex questions later. Questionnaires should be as clear and workable as possible, avoiding leading, complex, intellectual or irrelevant questions. Hence much time should be spent making them simple, clear, logical, interesting and attractive (**Figure 6.6**).

---

**I  Question content**

- Relevance and usefulness.
- Is more than one question needed for sufficient detail?
- Do the respondents know the information?
- Cultural transferability of question.
- Avoid bias.
- Is it too personal?

**II  Question wording**

- Is it clear?
- Does it make any prior assumption?
- Is it too impersonal?
- Is it too direct?

---

### III Form of response

- Can it best be answered with a multiple choice, scale or open answer?
- If there is a response checklist does it cover all alternatives?
- Is it uniform and/or adequate for the purpose?

### IV Sequence of questions

- Will the answer to a question be unduly influenced by the preceding question, i.e. is there autocorrelation (one result affects the next result)?
- Is the sequence logical?
- Are there interesting questions at the start to increase participant motivation to complete the questionnaire?

**Figure 6.6** Some considerations in the development of a questionnaire

1. Over the past ten years within the Republican movement there has been a definitive shift from armed struggle to electoral politics. Do you think this is a reflection of the movements doubts as to the political effectiveness of their campaign of violence?
2. What are your views on the IRA cease-fire declared on August 31 1994?
3. Do you think the Sinn Fein move was a genuine recognition of the futility of violence and as such a historical change of course, or was it merely a tactical gesture to entrap the British government?
4. The British Government stated that the IRA cease-fire was itself not enough to start movement to all party talks and that decommissioning of weapons was necessary. The Dublin view was that it was unrealistic to expect such a hand over from the IRA. Should decommissioning have ever been a precondition for talks?
5. In your opinion what is the political logic of the IRA?

**Figure 6.7** Extracts from a postal questionnaire

In **Figure 6.7** we perhaps see an example of a bad questionnaire. First, the questions are long, complex and intrusive. Surely, there would be many people not wishing to express their views on such an intricate and sensitive issue. Secondly, some of the questions are 'leading questions', such as question 3. It is hardly surprising that a postal questionnaire such as this received very few replies. Two examples of good, effective questionnaire are shown in **Figure 6.8**

## (a)

Street _____  Position _____

**Sex**
☐ male    ☐ Female

**Age**
☐ under 25   ☐ 26–40   ☐ 41–60   ☐ over 60

**What sort of housing do you live in?**
☐ council housing                ☐ privately rented (furnished)
☐ privately rented (unfurnished) ☐ owned flat
☐ owned house                    ☐ other (please specify) _____

**How long have you been living here?**
☐ under 6 months  ☐ 6–12 months  ☐ 1–2 years
☐ 3–5 years       ☐ over 5 years ☐ don't know

**How much longer do you expect to live here?**
☐ under 6 months  ☐ 6–12 months  ☐ 1–2 years
☐ 3–5 years       ☐ over 5 years ☐ don't know

**How would you rate this area on a scale of 1 to 5 in relation to: (1=bad  5=excellent  X=do not know)**

| | | |
|---|---|---|
| noise _____ | green areas _____ | healthcare _____ |
| pollution _____ | shops _____ | services for retired _____ |
| heavy traffic _____ | transport _____ | libraries _____ |
| crime _____ | recreation _____ | entertainment _____ |
| housing quality _____ | schools _____ | |

**On a scale of 1 to 5 please give your views on the attraction of the following area:**
**(1=not very desirable  5=very desirable  X=do not know)**

| | | |
|---|---|---|
| Hammersmith flyover _____ | West Kensington _____ | Shepherd's Bush _____ |
| Brook Green _____ | Brackenbury Village _____ | Fulham (riverside) _____ |
| Olympia _____ | Goldhawk Road _____ | Fulham (Queen's Club) _____ |

**Is the accommodation you have one that you occupy:**
☐ alone        ☐ with partner/spouse  ☐ with family with children
☐ with friends ☐ other                ☐ no response

Boxed annotations:
- Important when displaying results on maps afterwards
- Information which is basic but may explain people's differing attitudes to their area
- Will indicate the transience of the population which will affect housing quality
- Externalities that will affect housing quality
- To find out different opinions of areas which may help explain housing quality
- Will affect the transience of population of an area (family life-cycle model) and therefore the housing quality in the area

## (b)

1 How long have you lived in this area?
☐ 0–2 years   ☐ 3–5 years   ☐ 6–10 years   ☐ 11+ years

2 Where did you live prior to that?   town_____   borough_____

3 Is this your house:   ☐ privately rented   ☐ owner occupied   ☐ council rented

4 What renovations have you made?   ☐ loft extension   ☐ conservatory   ☐ redecorating
others (please specify) _____

5 How many people live in your house? _____    6 How many bedrooms? _____

7 What is your marital status?   ☐ single   ☐ married   ☐ divorced

8 With regard to work, do you consider yourself:   ☐ retired   ☐ part-time   ☐ full-time   ☐ unemployed

9 If part-time or full-time, what is your occupation and rank?_____

10 Do you have a car?  ☐ yes   ☐ no      Do you have a second car?  ☐ yes   ☐ no
year _____   make _____      year _____   make _____

11 Where do you work?_____

12 Mode of travel?   ☐ car   ☐ bus   ☐ tube   ☐ bike   ☐ walk

13 Do you have any children?   ☐ yes   ☐ no

14 If yes, how many? _____      how old _____

15 What school(s) do they go to?_____

16 Why did you choose to live here?
prices
proximity to:  communications
workplace
services
good restaurants
other _____
1 ☐☐☐☐☐ 5 (grid of rating boxes)

17 Why did you choose to live in this street? _____

**Figure 6.8** Extracts from two questionnaires: (a) on residential quality;
(b) on gentrification

**SECTION D**

# Interviews

It is quite common for the sort of topics tackled as part of the A-level Geography personal enquiry to require interviewing people such as local government officials, farmers, managers of firms, shopkeepers and so on. It has to be said that talking on a one-to-one basis can yield important information and useful insights.

An interview is by its nature more about questions of an open-ended nature. You stand to gain a lot by allowing the interviewee to volunteer information that you might not previously have thought relevant.

Here are some tips for successful interviewing:

- Always make an appointment for an interview by post, phone or a personal visit.
- Briefly explain in your communication why you want to meet the person concerned.
- It is helpful at this preliminary stage to give the interviewee some idea of the sorts of question you want to put.
- On the appointed day, turn up at the appointed time, and take some care over your appearance!
- Come along with a prepared list of questions or lines of enquiry, together with a pen and notebook for recording the information given during the interview.
- On meeting the interviewee, introduce yourself, express your appreciation that they are sparing you some of their time and give them a little bit of background to the interview (the A-level Geography requirement to undertake a personal enquiry, the topic you have chosen, what you hope to achieve, etc.).

- It is difficult to generalise about the ideal length for an interview, but do not overstay your welcome. Make sure you conduct the interview in a purposeful way and follow closely the guidelines you provided when making the appointment.
- When you have finished, thank the person once again and ask them whether they have any objections to their identity being revealed in the report, and whether they would like to be informed of your eventual findings.
- After the interview and when you come to analyse what has been said, look for any 'bias'. We all perceive the world from our own particular viewpoint, be it as a student, a manager or a local government official. Almost inevitably there arises a degree of divergence between perceptions and reality!

All this may seem just common sense –but it is surprising how often this does not prevail!

## Review

**4** Set out a framework (questions, lines of enquiry, data sought), etc. for an interview with the manager of a high-tech firm recently moved to a local science park. The aim of your project is to find out why your home town is proving so attractive to high-tech industry.

# Newspapers

Newspapers are an excellent source of information for Geographers. Take any newspaper, any day of the week and you will find a range of articles or reports dealing with environmental, social and economic issues, climate and weather, agriculture, inner cities, green belts, hazards and so on. National newspapers are useful as they allow us to see broad patterns at an international, national and regional level. The local press can also be an excellent source of information, views and debates on more local issues – it can be a veritable treasure-trove for the A-level personal enquiry. It is not just a matter of looking at the most recent issues. Most public libraries keep past copies (often on microfiche) and running back over years. Long runs of back numbers can become an important archive for many a personal enquiry topic. Don't be frightened to include the time dimension in your geographical investigation.

**Figures 6.9** and **6.10** are two newspaper extracts on the subject of crime. One is taken from a local newspaper, the *Oxford Mail*, and the other from a national paper, the *Guardian*. In short, we have two different perspectives on the same issue. What we have to do is extract the main points from each. To what extent do they accord? To what extent do they differ? What light does the national perspective throw on your personal enquiry into crime in Oxford? Read the following extracts carefully. In **Figure 6.9** the technique of highlighting salient points has been used. It is simple, and done properly, can be very effective in extracting the essence. But remember, this is only to be done to photocopies – NOT to books!

# Park and raid:
## Oxford Mail reveals your crime risk factor
## The car crime risk you take in Oxford's car parks

| Oxford City Car Parks | Theft of Vehicles | Theft from Vehicles | Criminal damage | Crime Total | No. of cars parked daily | Risk factor |
|---|---|---|---|---|---|---|
| Westgate | 36 | 243 | 106 | 385 | 3,102 | 12.4 |
| Gloucester Green | 3 | 4 | 3 | 10 | 328 | 3 |
| Worcester Green | 21 | 28 | 6 | 55 | 677 | 8.1 |

| Park and Ride car parks | Theft of Vehicles | Theft from Vehicles | Criminal damage | Crime Total | No. of cars parked daily | Risk factor |
|---|---|---|---|---|---|---|
| Pear Tree | 75 | 140 | 38 | 253 | 1,355 | 18.7 |
| Seacourt | 26 | 47 | 10 | 83 | 872 | 9.5 |
| Redbridge | 106 | 109 | 33 | 248 | 1,607 | 15.4 |
| Thornhill | 33 | 60 | 23 | 116 | 640 | 18.1 |

(Figures April 1996–:February 1997)

The Oxford Mail can reveal for the first time today the risk you take when you use the city's four park and ride car parks.

An extensive survey carried out by the paper shows motorists using the park and rides are up to SIX times more likely to be the victims of vehicle crime than those using the city centre car parks.

Top of the crime league is Pear Tree park and ride, in north Oxford. From April 1996 to February 1997 there were 75 cars stolen, 140 thefts from cars and criminal damage to 38 vehicles.

There were a total of 253 car crimes at Pear Tree compared to just 10 at Gloucester Green, in the city centre, over the same period.

The Oxford Mail has worked out an 'at risk' figure, which takes into account the number of cars using each car park. The number in the final column of our table –: the Risk Factor –: is a ratio of the total number of car crimes to the number of cars which use the car parks daily. The higher the figure, the greater your car is at risk from car crime. According to our research this make Gloucester Green six times safer.

The damaging statistics have prompted police to call for parking charges at the park and rides to pay for tighter security. Police chiefs want a fee of up to 50p introduced which will cover the cost of on-foot patrols by security guards.

Oxford City Council, which runs the park and rides, has been accused by departing Oxford police chief, Ralph Perry, of dragging its feet on the issue. 'Patrols' he said 'are currently limited to Thornhill and take place sporadically. But when private security guards are working there, crime drops to virtually zero. Any crime that does happen is in the early evening after the patrols have been taken out. I believe the answer is to introduce patrols and in quick time. If money is the stumbling block they should introduce a fee which would pay for the patrols.'

He said surveys showed the public willing to pay for the park and ride if it meant less chance of their cars being broken into or stolen.

Gill Sanders, the city council's chairman of highways and traffic committee, pointed out that more than a million cars use the park and rides each year putting the risk of car crime at less than one in a hundred, She said 'Although the figures are low, even one car crime is still one too many and car crime on park and ride sites is an issue we take very seriously. We are working hard with the police to improve systems and would like to improve security measures on all sites.'

One victim, whose car was stolen last week from Pear Tree said: 'Councillors are always telling us to use park and rides and are making it more and more difficult to park in Oxford. But they are just not safe. My daughter took the trouble of parking our car under a security camera. It didn't make any difference and we were parked there in daylight. If the council wants people to visit the city, they ought to get off their backsides and provide security patrols 16 hours a day. If it was co-ordinated security and somebody there the whole time, a charge would be reasonable, provided it was proper security and not just a patrol coming around once every few hours'.

John Arnold, the city council's director of property and technical services, said: 'We are aware that the public is supportive of a scheme to pay for any increased security on park and ride facilities and we are currently looking at the most effective way to put such schemes into place in the near future.'

**Figure 6.9** Extract from the *Oxford Mail*, April 1997

**Figure 6.10** Extract from the *Guardian*, 8 November 1995

# Fear of crime
## 'driving out high street shoppers'

**James Meikle** reports on the demise of town centres as customers opt for the safety and security of shopping malls.

Shoppers are deserting the high street for shopping malls because they fear crime and feel threatened by beggars, drunks and vagrants, researchers at Leicester University suggested yesterday. Three times as many town centre users saw crime and nuisance as serious problems than did customers in enclosed shopping centres, who welcomed the presence of closed circuit television and private security guards.

Crime against individuals did appear to be far greater on the street, say Andrew Beck and Andrew Willis, who surveyed the opinions of 622 shoppers in six towns and cities, 40 town centre managers, and 140 shopping centre managers. In a 12-month period there was six times as much crime suffered by shoppers in town centres (6 per cent) as in shopping centres (1 per cent).

They said high street retailers must make a radical reappraisal of priorities to stem the migration of worried shoppers to edge of town developments. The report is the latest to cast doubt on the future of the high street as shoppers seek more choice, comfort and safe car parking elsewhere.

John Gummer, the Environment Secretary, is determined to send a more positive message, suggesting that a 24-hour city or town centre with people living over businesses, vibrant night life, good lighting and safe car parks, offers real hope of urban revival.

The report also appeared to confirm public concern at begging and drunken behaviour, an issue fast rising up the political agenda. One in seven high street shoppers said they had avoided parts of the town centre, mostly around pubs and clubs, compared with one in twenty shopping centre shoppers. Three times as many town centre chiefs (30 per cent) consider crime and nuisance endemic than do shopping centre managers (10 per cent). The biggest problem the latter saw in malls was 'threatening youths'.

The report's authors said their findings indicated that significant privatisation of policing had already taken place with public support. 'The bobby on the beat may still patrol town centres but he or she has been superseded by the private security guard in the shopping mall . . . Both offer the presence of officers in uniform, which the public finds reassuring'.

Closed circuit television enjoyed widespread confidence despite lack of proven effectiveness. Security shutters were seen as necessary evils but awful to look at. At the moment town centre managers put commercial development of their areas above security of shoppers while mall managers saw safety as paramount. 'Retailers as well as local authorities and others with commercial interests in town centres will have to be prepared to fund any new style safe shopping strategies. It is unrealistic to expect town centre managers to deal with a problem without an adequate budget'.

## Review

5 Think of some topics where the use of backnumbers of local newspapers might be a useful source of information.

6 a Make a photocopy of **Figure 6.10**. Using a marker pen, highlight the salient points of the article.

b What points are common to both this and the article in **Figure 6.9**?

c In what ways do the local and national perspectives differ?

# Help from the PC

Most A-level students today regularly use personal computers. For Geography students, personal computers have much to offer:

- word processing;
- mapping packages;
- graphing packages;
- statistical packages;
- spreadsheets;
- data base handling;
- CD ROMs;
- access to the Internet.

One of the great strengths of computers is the speed with which they operate. Complex calculations can be completed in a matter of seconds. In addition, they have huge memory stores and they make vast amounts of data readily available. But it is important to remember that computers are only a tool. Examiners are not interested in testing what you know about computers, but what you know about Geography.

For the A-level Geography student, personal computers are probably most used in connection with the personal enquiry. There are many benefits. First, a word-processed report can look much better than one that is not. More importantly, it is easier to edit mistakes on a computer, rather than change whole pages of handwriting. Secondly, data bases can easily be developed for holding the data you collect. There is no limit to the amount of data that can be stored and later processed. Thirdly, spreadsheets allow us to make calculations easily and therefore analyse data more efficiently (**Chapter 2 section G**). Imagine how long it would take to analyse data using just a calculator. Fourthly, computers allow us to draw maps, graphs and diagrams and to experiment with different layouts and designs. There are many opportunities here, but there is just one more thing to stress: always remember to keep a backup copy of all your work. Too many people lose their work through the operational errors of hitting the wrong key and not backing up!

It may take time to learn the correct operating procedures of a computer, but once you have mastered them, you progress very fast and you can work that much quicker and more logically. There is a whole set of skills to be learnt here that will certainly serve you well beyond A-levels.

# The personal enquiry project

All A-level Geography students are required to complete a personal enquiry (this is given a variety of different names by the examinations boards) as part of their overall assessment. The personal enquiry is a prime opportunity for students to demonstrate their real worth, so far as many of the skills and techniques covered in this book are concerned. All Geography projects are required to follow very clear guidelines, laid down by the boards. It is strongly recommended that you find out about the specification (word length, mode of presentation, etc.) set by your particular examining board, together with any guidance notes and a copy of the marking scheme. Preferably you should do this before you make any sort of start; your teacher may already have assembled the requisite information.

As a general rule, the report based on your personal enquiry should be divided into four sections:

- introduction;
- methods of data collection;
- analysis and interpretation;
- conclusion.

The next four sections offer advice on each of these key stages.

**SECTION A**

## Introduction

This should have three main components:

- a clear statement of the aims of the project enquiry;
- scene setting and broader implications;
- data to be collected, and how.

### Aims

The paramount requirements of any personal enquiry are that it should be overtly geographical and have a clear focus. As for the latter, the topic and its aims should be made completely clear from the very beginning. There are a number of simple devices that can help to give the enquiry that sharp sense of purpose. The first is to pose the topic in the form of a **hypothesis**, for example:

- Pollution levels decrease downstream from the source of pollution.
- Rainfall reliability is greater in coastal locations.

- The steeper the slope angle, the thinner the soil.
- The pattern of social service provision changes with the ageing of a population.
- The incidence of DIY stores and garden centres increases away from the CBD.
- The pattern of crime in city X is directly related to poor housing.

As an alternative to a hypothesis, a question is another way of achieving focus, provided that the question is not too broad. The following give the flavour of what is required:

- What is the evidence that area A was once glaciated?
- How is the direction of air movement in town B modified by buildings?
- What changes occur across a belt of dunes?
- To what extent is trampling a problem along the C coastal path?
- What has been the pattern of migration into the new housing estate D?
- Why have high-tech firms chosen to move to the E science park?
- To what extent is village F a dormitory settlement?

It is often tempting to be rather ambitious, and to tackle more than one hypothesis or question. Some good general advice is to curb that ambition. You will not necessarily gain any more credit, and you certainly run the risk of diluting your enquiry's sense of purpose. Remember: better one hypothesis thoroughly tested, than two or three skimped!

## Scene-setting and broader implications

It is important to place your chosen enquiry topic in its geographical setting. There are two aspects to this. First, there is the task of describing the area in which the investigation is going to take place. Perhaps start by establishing the area's location – regionally and nationally. For physical studies, go on to describe the physical character of the area, its geology, relief, landforms, current and past processes, as well as soil and vegetation characteristics. For studies in human geography you might also portray the area in terms of its economic and social characteristics, such as land use, accessibility, settlement and population. It may well be appropriate to cover some of these aspects, even though your topic might lie in physical geography. Remember that people can have a significant impact on the physical environment.

The second dimension to the geographical background requires setting your study in its geographical context. You might do this by referring to the particular branch of Geography in which your topic lies. Does your topic relate to any particular issue or problem that is a current focus within that branch of Geography – for example, the impact of urban development on stream characteristics, or the incidence of poverty in cities? Will you be referring to any geographical theories and will you be using any models? If so, then now is the time to mention them. Here also is the opportunity to make reference to any articles or books you have read in order to explore the context of your chosen topic.

The examiners' reports compiled by most examination boards have shown that this matter of scene-setting and context are generally not well done. Why neglect it and waste valuable marks?

## Data to be collected and how

Having defined the topic and its aims, as well as its context, it is important now to clarify the following:

- The types of data needed for your enquiry.
- Which of these required data will be collected by fieldwork (**primary data**) and which from printed sources (**secondary data**).
- The type(s) of sampling procedure (e.g. random, systematic, stratified, transect, etc.) to be used in both types of data collection.
- Fieldwork methods and the equipment needed in the collection of primary data.
- The specific secondary sources you intend to research.
- The methods of statistical analysis to be applied to the raw data.

The key quality in the whole of this introductory section is clarity. You need to come across as someone who:

- has given the enquiry much careful consideration;
- has a clear idea of what they are doing;
- is well organised.

**SECTION B**

# Data collection

This again might be expected to have three main components:

- sampling and methods of collection;
- quality of data collected;
- discussion of any problems/difficulties.

## Sampling and methods of collection

Assuming that these two aspects were dealt with fairly briefly in your Introduction, and more in a spirit of what you hoped to do, now you should describe and explain in detail what actually happened.

You need to describe how the primary data were sampled, and why. You must justify your sampling methods and sample sizes. Secondary data will also have to be sampled, because it is impossible to read everything. So state how you came to choose the material you used.

Describe and justify your primary fieldwork methods – surveys, mapping, questionnaires, etc. Basically, describe how you went about things, and any equipment you may have used. Equally, describe and explain your reference to secondary sources, such as the Census, parish records, crime statistics, company data, local government publications, CD ROMs, etc.

## Quality of data collected

Here you should attempt to establish the reliability of your data – their accuracy, objectivity and general soundness in terms of possibly deriving valid conclusions. For example, would someone doing the same project in the area get the same or similar results? One aspect being called into question here is the key matter of sampling. For example, was the sample of people interviewed as part of your questionnaire survey too biased in favour of women, especially elderly women? Were you able to take soil samples at all the points designated by your sampling strategy? It is also necessary to acknowledge the limitations of data. For example, an investigation of crime needs to make clear that crime is frequently under-recorded. Information derived from interviews may well be subject to marked bias.

## Discussion of problems and/or difficulties

This might be called the 'confessional' bit. What you need to appreciate is that being honest about your work is a vital part of a critical approach. A critical approach to the personal enquiry, at all stages, is very much something that examiners and moderators are looking for – it is something for which you will be rewarded. Any practical problems experienced during the enquiry needs to be dealt with here. For example, were you able to obtain all the data you required, or to gain access to all the sites you wanted to examine? Any circumstances which made the collection of data difficult should be included here. It would also be well worth drawing attention to the ways you worked around or coped with these difficulties. This subsection should not just be an account of poor weather conditions, or a long-winded complaint that many people would not answer your questionnaire.

Support this section with diagrams illustrating your survey methods, photographs of the area in which primary data were collected, and perhaps even of you hard at work, as well as photocopies of your questionnaire, your interview framework or typical secondary source material.

# Analysis and interpretation

This is very much the heart of the enquiry, for it covers the analysis of your data and the interpretation of results. Sadly, it is a section where low marks are quite commonplace. Unfortunately it is virtually impossible to generalise much advice under this heading, for it is in this section that the uniqueness of each topic is most apparent.

Very much in the spotlight at this stage in the report are the analytical techniques that you have used. You should use a mix of techniques – statistical, cartographic and graphical (**Chapters, 2, 3, 4** and **5**), but try to resist the temptation to become too preoccupied with techniques. There is little to be gained from bombarding the same data set with a handful of slightly different analytical techniques. Furthermore, it is not necessary to spend much time describing each of the techniques you use. You can assume that the examiner is aware of them. Rather, you need to be confident on two important matters:

- that the techniques you use are right for the type of data and the line of enquiry;
- that you have you used them correctly.

From techniques, the spotlight shifts to interpretation. Again, you need to be sure on two counts:

- that accurate results have been extracted by the analytical techniques;
- that those results have been read and interpreted correctly.

A final thing to check is that the aim of the enquiry (its hypothesis or question) has been in focus throughout the analysis and interpretation. Try to report this whole section as clearly as possible by taking it in small steps. At each step, establish what you are trying to do, how you are doing it and what emerges. In this way, you will achieve a good integration of analysis and interpretation.

**SECTION D**

# Conclusion

This might involve three parts:

- a summary of the main findings;
- an evaluation of those conclusions;
- a discussion of the broader implications of the enquiry.

## Summary of the main findings

Having interpreted the results of your analyses, what are your most important findings. What do these results tell you?

## Evaluation of findings

How do these findings relate to the original hypothesis or question? Does the balance of your evidence support the hypothesis? Is the question answered to a satisfactory degree? This should be one major item in your evaluation. Others to be included in the discussion are an assessment of the reliability of the data you have collected and analysed, and the soundness of your analytical techniques. What sort of confidence limits can you set on your results? Are you able to identify future lines of enquiry that will push investigation of the topic in a profitable direction? If you had to repeat the enquiry (perish the thought), what would you do differently, and why?

## Broader implications

In this part you need to relate the results and conclusions you have derived from a small-scale study to the much larger scale. You need to return to the broader context that you dealt with back in the second part of the Introduction. For example, to what extent do your findings support or contradict any theories or models pertaining to the branch of Geography in which your topic lies? What light does your enquiry throw on broader contemporary issues? For example, do your findings suggest that there are differences or similarities between processes and outcomes at a local level and those at a national or international level? What are the wider implications of your findings – environmental, social, economic and political?

**SECTION E**

# Presentation

On the cover, you should print the title, your name and candidate number, the name of the school and its centre number. The cover should be carefully laid out and neatly presented.

Compile a Contents page on which you list the chapters, parts or sections into which your report is divided. These should be numbered, titled and the page number given where each starts. It is strongly recommended that you structure your report into the four parts indicated in the previous sections of this chapter.

Only write or type on one side of the A4 paper, and number all pages.

All maps and diagrams (with the exception of graphs) should be drawn on plain paper. The use of photocopied maps and diagrams is strongly discouraged by most boards. You will get credit for any maps and diagrams that you have drawn (provided they are relevant), but not for photocopies, which tend to spoil the presentation. Relevant photographs and sketches should also be integrated into the text.

All maps, diagrams, tables and photographs should have a title and be numbered in the order in which they are referred to in the text. They should all be labelled as 'figures'. It is also vital that they are integrated with the text by means of a figure reference; don't tuck them away at the back where they will be forgotten. The normal practice here is to insert '(Figure x)' at the end of the sentence dealing specifically with a particular point that is illustrated – make your illustrative material work for you by drawing the reader's attention to it at the relevant point. Examples of data sheets, questionnaires, statistical equations and so on used in the enquiry should be included, perhaps as part of an Appendix.

At the end of the project compile a bibliography – a full list of books, pamphlets, articles and so on that you have used in your project. These should be listed in alphabetical order by author. With some boards, marks are specifically reserved for the bibliography. You should also list any statistical packages or other computer software programs you have used.

Remember to provide a list of acknowledgements to people (including teachers, technicians and people you have interviewed), public bodies or organisations who helped you.

The standard of your English and your neatness are important. Carefully check your typing, spelling and grammar before handing in the report. Why not get someone else to check it through as well?

# Assessment

Finally, we thought it might be helpful to include some extracts from marking schemes used by two examination boards. These should give you some feel as to what is being assessed and what proportion of the total mark is being allocated to each particular aspect. Most of these extracts specify **mark-bands** or **levels of attainment**. Particular characteristics are specified and these are taken to indicate particular levels of attainment which deserve particular marks. The extracts are organised under the four major headings we have used above – introduction, data collection, analysis, explanation and interpretation, and conclusion.

## Introduction

**Statement of aims and objectives – 10 marks**

**8–10 marks** Includes introductory comments and references to source ideas. On the whole these may be based on a single hypothesis, question or issue backed up by reference to reading, a field course 'inspiration' and class notes. They will be placed within a syllabus area or areas. If the aim is very well set out, then this could score 10 marks. It may also be a well conceived idea or problem. Candidates will be able to justify the location of study in terms of the theoretical support. (7 + marks to those who make an extremely clear statement of a hypothesis or issue or aims related to a particular subject area of the syllabus.)

**0–1 mark** For aims and objectives which are garbled with no statement of the problem being tackled. Those that state 'this project is about ...' will come into this category. Field centre one-day projects will generally score here, or possibly in the next category. Two-village studies of a descriptive type are another example of poor aims. Poor background to topic.

Do not give much credit to overlong regurgitation of class notes/textbook sections on models, unless related to the study in hand and in the appropriate proportion.

**Figure 7.1** Two mark-bands used in assessing the introductory section (AEB, 1997)

**Investigation and design planning – 4 marks**

The candidate should make a clear statement of the question, issue or problem to be studied. The statement should include details of what techniques are considered to be appropriate and the data to be collected.

**4 marks** The candidate gives a clear statement of the aims of the project, with an understanding of the objectives, without assistance from the teacher. The choice of technique(s), data and style of presentation are justified.

**2 marks** The candidate needs some assistance to plan the investigation, and to select technique(s), data and style of presentation.

**Figure 7.2** Two mark-bands used in assessing the introductory section (London – Edexcel)

## Data collection

**Data collection – 25 marks**

**21–25 marks** A very clear summary of the methods of enquiry and data sources used. The methods are thorough and imaginative, given the restrictions of time and the level of enquiry and are well supported by ideas from the relevant literature. The data should be both primary data acquired by field observation and collection based on the correct procedures, and secondary data from official, referenced sources such as census material or water board data banks, etc. Correct and occasionally inspired use of equipment. Credit highly any detailed observations. Extremely well controlled use of a group acknowledged. Data for problem solving very well collected for this level of candidate.

**0–5 marks** Little or no knowledge of how to gather data. Material gathered haphazardly and indiscriminately with obvious, plugable gaps in the data, no matter what its source. No real appreciation that there should be an organised method of data collection. In many cases description will be a substitute for data.

**Figure 7.3** Two mark-bands used in assessing data collection (AEB, 1997)

**Data collection – 12 marks**

The candidate should show evidence of methodical research procedures, observation, practical skills, measurement and data collection. The data collection, whether primary or secondary, has to be the candidate's work. If the data is to be collected by groups or teacher assistance is used, each individual candidate must provide evidence of their own practical data collection.

**10–12 marks** The candidate follows a methodical research programme or makes observations and measurements in a careful and methodical without any assistance from the teacher. Practical skills and procedures are carried out in a rigorous way. The candidate takes account of all of the factors affecting the enquiry.

**4–6 marks** The candidate needs some assistance in carrying out the necessary research or in making observations and measurements, and in the carrying out of practical skills and procedures. The candidate takes account of some of the factors affecting the investigation.

**Figure 7.4** Two mark-bands used in assessing data collection (London – Edexcel)

## Analysis, and interpretation

**Skills and techniques – 25 marks**

**21–25 marks** Excellent use of appropriate skills and techniques, which can be cartographic, graphical and statistical. Obviously the candidate understands why techniques have been used and is aware of the shortcomings. Candidates are unlikely to score in this range unless they have some relevant statistical work, no matter how simple. There should be some reference to the source used for statistical techniques. Do not over-credit sledgehammers to crack nuts, or the over-use of techniques all showing the same result. Data will be used to make points. Excellent investigative technique of a problem where statistical techniques are inappropriate at this level.

**0–5 marks** No real use of any techniques other than a weak verbal description, perhaps supported by the odd map or diagram. Mere description based on historical sources might score 5 marks.

**Figure 7.5** Two mark-bands used in assessing skills and techniques (AEB, 1997)

**Relevance, interpretation and use of information – 25 marks**

**21–25 marks** The information is interpreted and used constructively to examine the hypothesis where it is presented in an accurate fashion with the maps, diagrams and statistics being integrated into the relevant parts of the text. All of the information is used and the interpretation is complete for the level of the project. Photographs are also interpreted and are seen to be relevant. Clear reference is made to existing theory and ideas developed in the aims. Alternative explanations appreciated and the aims continually recalled. The issue/problem is assessed and reassessed in the light of the data.

**0–5 marks** Information is lacking and interpretation shows all the signs of not understanding what the information shows. Very weak narrative and no attempt to relate to theory or even to the original issue placed before us.

**Figure 7.6** Two mark-bands used in assessing relevance, interpretation and use of information (AEB, 1997)

**Recording and analysis – 11 marks**

The candidate should show evidence that appropriate methods and techniques have been chosen to effectively research the topic chosen, and used to record, analyse and present the data collected.

**10–11 marks** The candidate is able to work without assistance from the teacher to collect and record the information or data with a high degree of accuracy and clarity, and there is a logical and coherent analysis of the data. The information is carefully and accurately presented.

**4–6 marks** The candidate requires some assistance with the recording of the information or data, and its analysis. The candidate shows evidence of some ability to organise and present the information in a logical way.

**Figure 7.7** Two mark-bands used in assessing data recording and analysis (London – Edexcel)

# Conclusion

**Conclusion – 10 marks**

**8–10 marks** Excellent summing up of a high quality project; it is able to evaluate how far the work has satisfied the hypotheses; is constructively self-critical of the work. An excellently resolved problem-solving exercise; is able to offer constructive proposals for further development or uses of the study.

**0 marks** No conclusion or attempt to pull material together.

**Figure 7.8** Two mark-bands in assessing conclusions (AEB, 1997)

**Interpretation and conclusions – 13 marks**

The candidate should show a degree of clarity of expression, logical structure and coherent presentation of ideas in their evaluation and interpretation of the information or data collected as part of the personal enquiry.

**10–13 marks** The candidate works without assistance from the teacher to use the information or data to make logical and coherent evaluations. Complex ideas are expressed fluently and extremely clearly. There is evidence of the ability to find significant explanations and present arguments which are consistently relevant and well structured in order to draw effective conclusions. There will be few if any errors of grammar, punctuation and spelling.

**4–6 marks** With some assistance, the candidate can achieve limited progress in the evaluation and the use of the information or data collected. Straightforward ideas will be expressed clearly but not always fluently and arguments may stray from the point or be weakly presented. With some assistance simple conclusions are made. Sentences and paragraphs may be well connected and there may be some errors in grammar, punctuation and spelling.

**Figure 7.9** Two mark-bands used in assessing interpretation and conclusions (London – Edexcel)

Finally, the point needs to be made that the precise weighting of the personal enquiry in the context of the overall examination in A-level Geography varies from board to board. So too do the individual criteria used in that assessment and their relative weighting. That should have become evident in the above extracts. However, **Figure 7.10** probably gives what we might call an average picture.

| | |
|---|---:|
| **1 Planning** | **[6 marks]** |
| ■ Clear statement of hypothesis or hypotheses | 2 |
| ■ Selection of data required | 2 |
| ■ Evidence of planning of techniques of data collection and analysis | 2 |
| | |
| **2 Data collection and representation** | **[12 marks]** |
| ■ Data collection techniques (including sampling if appropriate) | 6 |
| ■ Awareness of limitations in data collection and quality | 3 |
| ■ Representation of data | 3 |
| | |
| **3 Analysis and explanation** | **[10 marks]** |
| ■ Application of descriptive and analytical techniques | 5 |
| ■ Description and interpretation of results | 5 |
| | |
| **4 Conclusion** | **[9 marks]** |
| ■ Summary and relation to original aims | 3 |
| ■ Evaluation of interpretation of data analysis | 3 |
| ■ Relating findings to general contextual background | 3 |
| | |
| **5 Organisation and presentation** | **[3 marks]** |
| | |
| | TOTAL 40 |

**Figure 7.10** An examiner's mark sheet

Short of doing the enquiry for you, that is about as far as we can go by way of helping you. After all, it is meant to be an individual effort! So, good luck!

# Appendix

TABLE 1

## Spearman's rank correlation coefficient levels of significance

| | Significance | |
|---|---|---|
| **N** | **95%** | **99%** |
| 4 | 1.00 | - |
| 5 | 0.90 | 1.00 |
| 6 | 0.83 | 0.94 |
| 7 | 0.71 | 0.89 |
| 8 | 0.64 | 0.83 |
| 9 | 0.60 | 0.78 |
| 10 | 0.56 | 0.75 |
| 12 | 0.51 | 0.71 |
| 14 | 0.46 | 0.65 |
| 16 | 0.43 | 0.60 |
| 18 | 0.40 | 0.56 |
| 20 | 0.38 | 0.53 |
| 22 | 0.36 | 0.51 |
| 24 | 0.34 | 0.49 |
| 26 | 0.33 | 0.47 |
| 28 | 0.32 | 0.45 |
| 30 | 0.31 | 0.42 |

**TABLE 2**

# The chi-squared test

The critical values of chi square given below show the probability that the calculated value of $\chi^2$ is the result of a chance distribution. The larger value of $\chi^2$ the smaller the probability that $H_0$ is correct.

| df | 0.10 | 0.05 | 0.01 | 0.001 | df | 0.10 | 0.05 | 0.01 | 0.001 |
|----|------|------|------|-------|----|------|------|------|-------|
| 1 | 2.71 | 3.84 | 6.64 | 10.83 | 16 | 23.54 | 26.30 | 32.00 | 39.29 |
| 2 | 4.60 | 5.99 | 9.21 | 13.82 | 17 | 24.77 | 27.59 | 33.41 | 40.75 |
| 3 | 6.25 | 7.82 | 11.34 | 16.27 | 18 | 25.99 | 28.87 | 34.80 | 42.31 |
| 4 | 7.78 | 9.49 | 13.28 | 18.46 | 19 | 27.20 | 30.14 | 36.19 | 43.82 |
| 5 | 9.24 | 11.07 | 15.09 | 20.52 | 20 | 28.41 | 31.41 | 37.57 | 45.32 |
| 6 | 10.24 | 12.59 | 16.81 | 22.46 | 21 | 29.62 | 32.67 | 38.93 | 46.80 |
| 7 | 12.02 | 14.07 | 18.48 | 24.32 | 22 | 30.81 | 33.92 | 40.29 | 48.27 |
| 8 | 13.36 | 15.51 | 20.09 | 26.12 | 23 | 32.01 | 35.17 | 41.64 | 49.73 |
| 9 | 14.68 | 16.92 | 21.67 | 27.88 | 24 | 33.20 | 36.42 | 42.98 | 51.18 |
| 10 | 15.99 | 18.31 | 23.21 | 29.59 | 25 | 34.38 | 37.65 | 44.31 | 52.62 |
| 11 | 17.28 | 19.68 | 24.72 | 31.26 | 26 | 35.56 | 38.88 | 45.64 | 54.05 |
| 12 | 18.55 | 21.03 | 26.22 | 32.26 | 27 | 36.74 | 40.11 | 46.96 | 55.48 |
| 13 | 19.81 | 22.36 | 27.69 | 34.53 | 28 | 37.92 | 41.34 | 48.28 | 56.89 |
| 14 | 21.06 | 23.68 | 29.14 | 36.12 | 29 | 39.09 | 42.56 | 49.59 | 58.30 |
| 15 | 22.31 | 25.00 | 30.58 | 37.70 | 30 | 40.26 | 43.77 | 50.89 | 59.70 |

**TABLE 3**

# Random number table

|    | 17 | 42 | 28 | 23 | 17 | 59 | 66 | 38 | 61 | 02 | 10 |
|----|----|----|----|----|----|----|----|----|----|----|----|
|    | 10 | 51 | 55 | 92 | 52 | 74 | 49 | 04 | 49 | 03 | 04 |
| 33 | 53 | 70 | 11 | 54 | 48 | 63 | 50 | 90 | 37 | 21 | 46 |
| 77 | 84 | 87 | 67 | 39 | 95 | 85 | 54 | 97 | 37 | 33 | 41 |
| 11 | 75 | 74 | 90 | 50 | 08 | 91 | 12 | 44 | 82 | 40 | 30 |
| 62 | 45 | 50 | 64 | 54 | 65 | 17 | 89 | 25 | 59 | 44 | 64 |
| 59 | 33 | 23 | 31 | 39 | 84 | 54 | 33 | 20 | 76 | 25 | 50 |
| 04 | 15 | 26 | 89 | 98 | 17 | 52 | 53 | 82 | 62 | 02 | 21 |
| 82 | 34 | 13 | 41 | 03 | 68 | 97 | 81 | 40 | 72 | 61 | 52 |
| 40 | 49 | 27 | 56 | 49 | 79 | 34 | 34 | 32 | 22 | 60 | 53 |
| 91 | 17 | 08 | 72 | 87 | 46 | 75 | 73 | 00 | 11 | 27 | 07 |
| 05 | 20 | 30 | 85 | 22 | 21 | 04 | 67 | 95 | 97 | 98 | 62 |
| 17 | 27 | 31 | 42 | 64 | 71 | 64 | 00 | 26 | 04 | 66 | 91 |
| 03 | 64 | 59 | 07 | 42 | 95 | 81 | 39 | 06 | 41 | 29 | 81 |
| 90 | 32 | 70 | 17 | 72 | 03 | 61 | 66 | 26 | 24 | 71 | 97 |
| 27 | 26 | 08 | 79 | 61 | 03 | 62 | 93 | 23 | 29 | 26 | 04 |
| 50 | 14 | 30 | 85 | 38 | 97 | 56 | 37 | 08 | 12 | 23 | 07 |
| 61 | 05 | 92 | 08 | 29 | 94 | 10 | 96 | 50 | 01 | 33 | 85 |
| 66 | 28 | 02 | 45 | 37 | 89 |    |    |    |    |    |    |

## TABLE 4

# Sample size calculator

Range of error of estimates of population with one characteristic at 95% confidence limits (percentage plus or minus).

| percentage affirmative | sample sizes | | | | | | | | | | | | | |
|---|---|---|---|---|---|---|---|---|---|---|---|---|---|---|
| | 25 | 50 | 100 | 200 | 300 | 400 | 500 | 800 | 1 000 | 2 000 | 5 000 | 25 000 | 50 000 |
| 98% or 2% | 5.6 | 4 | 2.8 | 2 | 1.6 | 1.4 | 1.3 | 0.98 | 0.9 | 0.61 | 0.4 | 0.18 | 0.11 |
| 97% or 3% | 6.8 | 4.9 | 3.4 | 2.4 | 2 | 1.7 | 1.5 | 1.2 | 1.1 | 0.75 | 0.49 | 0.22 | 0.14 |
| 96% or 4% | 7.8 | 5.6 | 3.9 | 2.8 | 2.3 | 2 | 1.8 | 1.4 | 1.3 | 0.86 | 0.56 | 0.25 | 0.16 |
| 95% or 5% | 8.7 | 6.2 | 4.4 | 3.1 | 2.5 | 2.2 | 2 | 1.5 | 1.4 | 0.96 | 0.62 | 0.27 | 0.17 |
| 94% or 6% | 9.5 | 6.8 | 4.8 | 3.4 | 2.8 | 2.4 | 2.1 | 1.7 | 1.5 | 1 | 0.68 | 0.3 | 0.19 |
| 92% or 8% | 10.8 | 7.7 | 5.4 | 3.8 | 3.1 | 2.7 | 2.4 | 1.9 | 1.7 | 1.2 | 0.77 | 0.34 | 0.22 |
| 90% or 10% | 12 | 8.5 | 6 | 4.3 | 3.5 | 3 | 2.7 | 2.1 | 1.9 | 1.3 | 0.85 | 0.38 | 0.24 |
| 88% or 12% | 13 | 9.2 | 6.5 | 4.6 | 3.8 | 3.3 | 2.9 | 2.3 | 2.1 | 1.4 | 0.92 | 0.41 | 0.26 |
| 85% or 15% | 14.3 | 10.1 | 7.1 | 5.1 | 4.1 | 3.6 | 3.2 | 2.5 | 2.3 | 1.6 | 1 | 0.45 | 0.29 |
| 80% or 20% | 16 | 11.4 | 8 | 5.7 | 4.6 | 4 | 3.6 | 2.8 | 2.5 | 1.8 | 1.1 | 0.5 | 0.32 |
| 75% or 25% | 17.3 | 12.3 | 8.7 | 6.1 | 5 | 4.3 | 3.9 | 3 | 2.8 | 1.9 | 1.2 | 0.55 | 0.35 |
| 70% or 30% | 18.3 | 13 | 9.2 | 6.5 | 5.3 | 4.6 | 4.1 | 3.2 | 2.9 | 2 | 1.3 | 0.58 | 0.37 |
| 65% or 35% | 19.1 | 13.5 | 9.5 | 6.8 | 5.5 | 4.8 | 4.3 | 3.3 | 3.1 | 2.1 | 1.4 | 0.6 | 0.38 |
| 60% or 40% | 19.6 | 13.9 | 9.8 | 7 | 5.7 | 4.9 | 4.4 | 3.4 | 3.1 | 2.2 | 1.4 | 0.62 | 0.39 |
| 55% or 45% | 19.8 | 14.1 | 9.9 | 7 | 5.8 | 5 | 4.5 | 3.5 | 3.2 | 2.2 | 1.4 | 0.62 | 0.4 |
| 50% | | 20 | 14.2 | 10 | 7.1 | 5.8 | 5 | 4.5 | 3.5 | 3.2 | 2.2 | 1.4 | 0.63 |